A GUIDE TO THE

ISLAMIC POTTERY

OF THE NEAR EAST

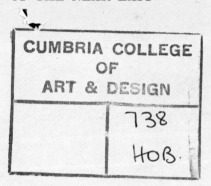

Fig. 100. TURKISH MOSQUE LAMP DATED 1549

BRITISH MUSEUM

A GUIDE TO THE
ISLAMIC POTTERY
OF THE NEAR EAST

BY
R. L. HOBSON, C.B.

With 40 Plates and 73 Illustrations

PRINTED BY ORDER OF THE TRUSTEES
1932

PREFACE

LIKE the other ceramic collections in this Department, the Near-Eastern was started by Sir Wollaston Franks. The Henderson Bequest in 1878 brought important accessions especially in the later Persian and the Turkish sections, and Mr. F. Du Cane Godman and Mr. Henry Wallis both contributed useful material at the end of the last century. There have been many additions made during the past fifteen years, especially in the wares of the first period; and Mr. Henry Van den Bergh has given specimens from time to time, which are now assembled in two pillar-cases in Bay XXVI.

The Collection includes examples of most of the known types of Near-Eastern wares, providing good material for historical study. It is not without objects of high quality and great artistic merit in the Persian and Syrian sections, while in the Turkish wares it reaches an exceptionally high standard. This part of the Collection is distinguished by a document of capital importance, the famous lamp from the Mosque of Omar in Jerusalem with its inscription stating that it was made in the year 956 of the Hijra (=A.D. 1549) and that the painter of it was 'the poor, the humble Muṣṭafa'.

With regard to the classification, it is not yet possible, with our limited knowledge, to group the material by factories or even, except in a few cases, by districts. For the purposes of this Guide a tentative arrangement in three periods has been made in order to show as far as possible the stages of development of the different kinds of ware; but even so we have not felt bound to adhere rigidly to this general plan where it seemed preferable to complete the account of some special ware in one chapter.

Very little of the Near-Eastern pottery made in the earlier periods has been preserved above ground. Most of it has been recovered in a fragmentary condition from the sites of ruined cities, and intact specimens are few. Needless to say the restoration of the broken pieces cannot always be complete, and many liberties have been taken in the preparation of specimens for the market. In these circumstances special importance attaches to fragments, and in particular to those which have come from authenticated finds. A useful series of these fragments is exhibited in the Table-Case of Bay XXVII and in the drawers of Table-Case H.

The rest of the Collection occupies Pier-Cases D, E, F, and part of the Table-Case in Bay XXVIII, Pier-Cases A, B, C of Bay XXVII, Table-Case H, and Standard-Case I in which some of the larger and more imposing pieces are shown. The Turkish pottery fills Pier-Cases D, E, F of Bay XXVII and A, B, C of Bay XXVI. Tiles are shown on the pillars between the Bays, along the top of one Pier-Case, and in the shallow cases on the Bridge.

Where colour is such an important feature of the ware, it is regrettable that only half-tone illustrations are possible in these low-priced Guide-books; but attention is drawn to two series of coloured postcards, the one (C 14) chiefly Persian and the other (B 23) Turkish.

For assistance in the preparation of this Guide I am indebted to the staff of this Department, and to Mr. A. S. Fulton of the Department of Oriental Printed Books and Manuscripts who has corrected the romanization of Eastern words and names.

R. L. HOBSON, KEEPER

*Department of Ceramics
and Ethnography*

February, 1932.

CONTENTS

LIST OF ILLUSTRATIONS

PLATE I

FIG. 1. AMPHORA: PROBABLY THIRD CENTURY

INTRODUCTION

THE Persian Exhibition has come and gone. For two months it filled Burlington House with wondering crowds and then it melted away as if at the touch of a genie. It was the first comprehensive view we have had in England of Persian art, and it left an impression of great splendour, of abundant colour, and of intricate but pleasing designs.

One of the outstanding features was the pottery, of which there was a representative display covering all periods from prehistoric to modern times. The pigmented pottery of Susa and Nihavand showed the surprisingly mature pictorial decoration of a period not later than the third millennium B.C. The first sign of glaze appeared on vessels of the neo-Babylonian period (seventh to sixth century B.C.), also from Susa. This was followed by pottery with green or greenish blue glaze (cf. fig. 1) made in the Parthian (248 B.C.–A.D. 226) and early Sassanian[1] (A.D. 226–641) periods. But these things were merely preludes to the large and varied display which illustrated the brilliant ceramic developments of the Islamic age.

The Islamic pottery of Persia and the Near East holds a very high position in the world of ceramics. If it falls short of the supreme technical achievements of Chinese porcelain, it certainly compares favourably with Chinese pottery and with the pottery of any nation in Europe. The high-fired porcelain glazes are capable of developing colours more intense and positive: the transparent enamels of the Chinese *famille verte* porcelain are brighter and more sparkling; but the Persian pottery glazes have a soft luxuriance of colour which is hardly equalled on any other ceramic medium, and the mat Rhages polychrome enamels have a subdued splendour that renders them peculiarly attractive. The decorative scheme of painting in still black under a pale turquoise blue glaze has been nowhere exploited with such success as in the Near East; while the polychrome Turkish pottery with its bold designs in opaque red and luminous blue is without parallel and perhaps without equal in its own class.

The principal triumphs of the Near-Eastern potters have been achieved with a ware of sandy white material covered with a transparent, silicious glaze, both of them peculiar to the Near East. The ware is soft and loose-grained and does not lend itself readily to thin potting or perfect evenness of surface; and the glaze is thick and fluid, running into pools in the hollow parts

---

[1] Much uncertainty exists with regard to Sassanian pottery. It has not yet been effectively segregated from the Parthian, late Roman, and early Islamic wares.

and often ending in heavy drops short of the base of the vessel. The potters evidently took little account of mechanical accuracy of finish; and a robust ruggedness, which is shared by some of the most reputable pottery of the Far East, does not in any way detract from its merits. This is true especially of the wares of the earlier periods. From the sixteenth century onwards the pottery tends to become closer-grained and smoother, and often harder. When deeply penetrated with the glassy constituents of the glaze and fired strongly enough for vitrification, it assumes the character of a translucent 'soft paste' porcelain. In exceptional cases, where the body material is unusually compact and strongly fired, the ware has even been taken for true kaolinic porcelain such as was imported from China; but until a specimen of undoubted Persian origin has been proved by analysis to consist of kaolin and petuntse, the elements of Chinese porcelain, we shall not be able to accept the statement that true porcelain was ever made in Persia.

The debt of Persia to China in any case is a large one. From the early years of Islam, Mohammedan merchants traded in the Far East, and we read of an Arab settlement in Canton in the eighth century. The Chinese in their turn visited Western Asia, and material evidence of the importation of Chinese pottery and porcelain into Mesopotamia in the ninth century is given by the excavations at Sāmarrā (p. 6). The influence of this imported ware is apparent in the locally made Sāmarrā pottery. The Chinese, on the other hand, took something back from Persia. Certain early Chinese pottery shapes show unmistakably Persian influence. Certain techniques, such as the *graffiato* described on p. 24 and the use of enamels on the glaze, seem to have developed in Persia earlier than in China. Painting in cobalt blue is more advanced on the Sāmarrā pottery than on any known Chinese specimen of even date; and it is common knowledge that in the fifteenth century the Chinese obtained their best cobalt blue (their 'Mohammedan blue') from the Near East. For the rest the influence of China was felt in a steadily increasing degree from the thirteenth century, the time of the Mongol invasions, onwards, until in the sixteenth and seventeenth centuries the Persian potter's chief aim seems to have been to appear as Chinese as possible.

But there is one technique employed in the Near East which has no counterpart in China, that of decoration in lustre pigments (see p. 3). For good or evil this was a contribution of the Near East to the potter's stock-in-trade. How and where it came into being is not yet known and perhaps never will be. That lustred pottery was originally devised as a cheap substitute for precious metal is likely enough. Some of the earliest specimens have embossed designs of metallic derivation and an over-all lustre which creates the illusion of a metal surface. The intention is not so obvious in the pottery with painted decoration in lustre, which developed from this, but it is significant that one of the oldest descriptions of it is 'golden earthenware'.

Whether the lustre technique was known in pre-Islamic times is not yet clearly determined. No serious evidence has so far been produced of its appearance on pre-Islamic pottery, but there are one or two fragments of lustred glass found in Egypt and Syria for which an earlier date has been claimed chiefly on stylistic grounds.[1] All we know for certain is that the technique was fully developed by the ninth century (p. 3) and that it was freely exploited on Near-Eastern pottery from then onwards.

The artistic value of lustre painting as a ceramic decoration is questioned by many critics. It is not to every one's taste. But it is generally agreed that the Near-Eastern potters have made better use of it than those of any other country; and even the severest critics admit the splendour of the broad expanses of lustred tile-work in mosques and public buildings.

The influence of Near-Eastern pottery in Europe was extensive. It is observed in many subtle forms in the early maiolica of Italy, whence it spread to other parts. It is most apparent in Spain, whither it came as a natural sequel to the Moorish invasion, the arts of the Near East having followed the advance of Islam along North Africa. Indeed the Spanish-Moorish pottery (see Bay XXVI West) is essentially Near-Eastern in feeling and has little in common with the contemporary wares of the rest of Europe. Here again lustre painting is one of the chief methods of decoration; and it seems that this technique passed from Spain into Italy, where it was adopted at Deruta and Gubbio at the end of the fifteenth century.

It would be interesting to trace the origin of the various processes employed by the Islamic potters. The simple appliances of the trade, such as the wheel for making rounded forms, moulds for more intricate shapes and for relief ornament, the stylus and the knife for incising decorative designs and the like, were now common property. Lead glaze had been freely used on late Roman pottery; green and blue silicious glazes on Parthian earthenware; the Egyptians had used opaque ceramic pastes of turquoise blue, yellow, and red colours which show that the use of metallic oxides as colouring agents had long been understood, and they used the brush to decorate turquoise blue grounds with designs in manganese. But Islamic pottery differs from its forerunners in many striking features, such as the development of the *graffiato* technique, and of polychrome decoration in slips (liquid clays), coloured glazes, enamels, and lustre. For some of these processes it was indebted to China. The T'ang pottery with

[1] C. J. Lamm, *Mittelalterliche Gläser*, Berlin, 1930, p. 111.

decoration incised in outline and filled in with coloured glazes has its counterpart in some of the early pottery found in Northern Persia[1] and in the beautiful ware of which fig. 20 is an example; and the mottled T'ang glazes were copied on the pottery found at Sāmarrā, Susa, Samarkand, and elsewhere.

In regard to the other polychrome processes priority seems to rest with the Near East, but where they were first used is not yet clear. One naturally looks to some great centre of civilization such as was Byzantium in the centuries immediately preceding Islam; and though we have little knowledge at present of Byzantine pottery prior to the tenth, or possibly ninth, century, there are some specimens published by Mr. Talbot Rice[2] which may help us in our quest. These are the tenth-century plaques and other objects decorated in polychrome on a white or pinkish white body. Of these the ikon[3] of St. Theodore from Patleina, Bulgaria, which is painted in manganese brown, brownish yellow, and an earthy ochreous red, and the similarly coloured fragments on Plate III of Mr. Rice's book, have affinities with the polychrome bowls which are variously attributed to Āmul and Samarkand. Other Byzantine plaques of the same period are decorated with heavy brown outlines filled in with blue, green, and yellow under a transparent lead glaze, and in some cases leaf-gilding is added. These last seem to antedate our Persian specimens of similar technique; while on some of the Byzantine polychrome pottery ranging from the tenth to the thirteenth century free use was made of a thick, upstanding red of the same nature as the red of the sixteenth-century Turkish ware (p. 87). There is no sign of the growth of this kind of polychrome in Egypt, and on the whole such indications as we have at present suggest that it derives from Byzantine sources.

The *graffiato* technique (see p. 24) was also used by the Byzantine potters; but there is no evidence as yet that it originated with them. Indeed priority of existing specimens belongs to Persia. With regard to lustre, there is no trace of its use on Chinese or Byzantine pottery, and we must look for its evolution in Persia, Mesopotamia, or Egypt.

[1] *Burlington Magazine*, March 1931, 'Pottery notes from the Persian Exhibition,' Plate I A.

[2] *Byzantine Glazed Pottery*, 1930.   [3] *Ibid.*, Frontispiece.

PERIOD I

(From A.D. 622 to 1200).

HISTORY is all but silent on the doings of the early Islamic potters, and we are forced to seek our enlightenment from the earth, which has proved such a fertile source of information in so many other fields of archaeology. In this field, too, it would doubtless be highly productive if systematic excavation were carried out on likely sites. Excavation there has been in plenty, but unfortunately it has been conducted furtively and with a view to private gain, and the results have been scant and elusive. The sites of old cities which were destroyed in the Mongol invasion of the thirteenth century, or which were abandoned long ago for other reasons, have been searched by treasure hunters who were more anxious to conceal than to impart information. And so large quantities of material, pottery whole or fragmentary, mostly pieced together and arbitrarily restored, have come on the market with only vague and unreliable hints as to their age and origin. Thus the ruins of Rakka and Rhages are honeycombed with holes made by casual diggers, and only occasionally have they been examined by responsible persons. The waste-heaps of Fostāṭ in Egypt have yielded myriads of fragments of pottery of all periods, but here in spite of serious attempts to exploit the site scientifically the absence of any regular stratification of the deposits has robbed the rich material of much of its evidential value. The most valuable contributions have been made by Professors Sarre and Herzfeld working at Rakka, Baalbek, and other sites in Syria and Mesopotamia, and above all at Sāmarrā; by the French Mission at Susa; by M. de Lorey at Rakka and Damascus; and by the late Aly Bey Bahgat at Cairo. Minor excavations at Āfrāsiyāb, a suburb of Samarkand, and on the ruins of Brahminabad in India have produced valuable material, and the work of the French scientists in Moorish Africa and of Spaniards at Medīnat az-Zahrā in southern Spain have all contributed something to the general store of information on early Islamic pottery.

The task of the historian to-day is to piece together the scattered bits of information gleaned from these various sources, coherently enough to explain the specimens in our collections. Doubtless the story will grow clearer and more complete when further excavations have been made by responsible persons. Meanwhile there is one real source of light to which we can turn, and that is the work done by Professors Sarre and Herzfeld at Sāmarrā.

B

SĀMARRĀ

In 838 the Caliph Muʿtaṣim, weary of the dust and tumult of Bagdad, built a luxurious residence at Sāmarrā, about sixty miles higher up the Tigris. Forty-five years later his successor returned to Bagdad, and the star of Sāmarrā set as rapidly as it had risen. The royal buildings were abandoned and allowed to fall into ruins, in which condition they remained almost undisturbed till the twentieth century, when two sets of excavations were made in them by Professors Sarre and Herzfeld. These excavations were systematically carried out, and the results have been and are being published in detail in Berlin. Consequently the material found there is of real scientific value and gives us one of the few satisfactory *points d'appui* which exist in the study of early Islamic art.

The pottery found on the palace sites may be assumed to belong to the forty-five years between 838 and 883. It doubtless represents the best and most refined ceramic productions available at the time; and though only fragments of it now remain, they give us a good idea of its variety and artistic quality. The bulk of it has a close-grained, soft, buff earthenware body, not unlike that of Italian maiolica, and so frequent is this type that the habit has already grown of calling it the Sāmarrā body. There is, however, no positive proof that it was made at Sāmarrā rather than at Bagdad or some other easily accessible centre. The only actual kiln-remains were found in the district of Kura on the outskirts of old Sāmarrā, and these seem to belong to a slightly later period. Moreover, practically all the Sāmarrā types have also been unearthed at Susa and Rhages in Persia, most of them at Fosṭāṭ in Egypt, and some at Rakka. But we shall return to this question later.

The Sāmarrā finds include many pieces of unglazed pottery which will be discussed in another section dealing with wares of that kind (p. 32). The glazed pottery is very varied. It includes that very widespread type of coarse buff pottery with green or greenish blue glaze which seems to have been continuously made in the Near East from Parthian times onwards. The wares are either plain or decorated with simple incised patterns or rough applied reliefs consisting of crinkled or wavy bands, &c. A vase of this class (fig. 1), though not from Sāmarrā, is shown in the end of Table-case H; it belongs to the Sassanian period.

Another ware which recalls the late Roman pottery found in the Near East has a fine-grained red body thinly potted and ornamented with sharply moulded reliefs covered with a green or yellow glaze (fig. 2). Two little fragments of this ware in a perfect state of preservation (fig. 3) show that it was sometimes completely covered with a metallic lustre giving it a golden appearance.

PLATE II

FIGS. 2–6. FRAGMENTS FROM SĀMARRĀ AND EGYPT

Indeed the general appearance of the ware and its characteristic ornament suggest that it was an imitation of metal-work. In many cases the lustre has almost disappeared from wear or burial, and the little that remains has been mistaken for irides-

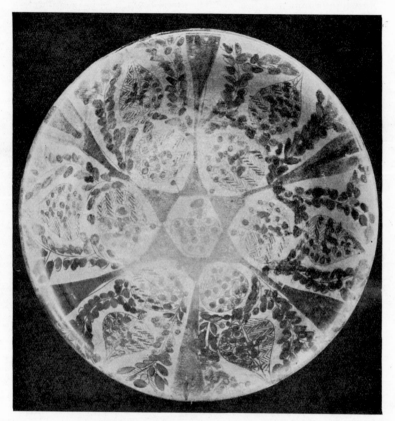

Fig. 7. Basin with lustre decoration. 9th century.

cence.[1] This class of ware has also been found at Susa, Rhages, and Fosṭāṭ.

Pottery with designs painted in lustre pigment[2] is among the

---

[1] One writer has gone so far as to deny the existence of lustre on this class of pottery: but the brilliant little fragments mentioned above leave no doubt about the matter.

[2] The lustre is formed by painting on the glazed surface a pigment formed of metallic salts (copper, silver, and perhaps other metals were used) which, when fired at a low temperature in a special kind of kiln, deposit a thin

most interesting and important of the Sāmarrā finds. The lustre in this case, though essentially the same as that mentioned in the preceding paragraph, is differently applied. Instead of covering the entire surface with a deposit of metal,[1] it is painted on with a brush in ornamental designs. The lustre itself, too, has a different appearance, partly no doubt because it is laid on a different kind of ware. The ware in this case has the so-called Sāmarrā body, a fine-grained, pale buff earthenware coated with an opaque, cream white glaze which is backed with white slip.[2] The pinkish colour

FIG. 8. Fragment of a lustred tile from Sāmarrā.

of so much of this glaze to-day is probably due mainly to burial. The Sāmarrā lustre colours have a remarkably wide range: there is a blood-red lustre with ruby reflections, a golden lustre, a brown lustre, a golden brown lustre, and an olive green lustre, and they were all clearly produced at will, because we find them skilfully combined on the same piece. At a later date when the use of lustre was very general its colour was much more uniform, and it is surprising to find that the technique was far more complex in this early period. The designs are rather crowded (fig. 7) and there is a tendency to fill all the spaces with close diaper patterns—

film of metal on the glaze. If the film is thin enough to allow the light to penetrate it, the lustre glows with rainbow reflections.

[1] It is not to be inferred that in the class of ware described in this section the lustre was not applied as a monochrome as well. In the Table-case in Bay XXVII are pieces of dishes with blood-red lustre evenly spread over their surface.

[2] The lustre is generally on this cream ground, but there were a few fragments found with lustre on a blue glaze.

trelliswork, scale, network, hatching—the object clearly being to get the greatest possible play of the lustre colours.

Besides being used on cups, dishes, and various kinds of vessels the lustre pigments were effectively applied to wall decoration on large slabs or tiles. Fragments of these tiles in the Table-case in Bay XXVII have a fine design of a wreath enclosing a bird (fig. 8): others have a sprinkled or marbled ground: and others are painted with bold scrolls and foliage in a very dark brown which seems to have been originally lustre (fig. 9).

FIG. 9. Fragment of a tile from Sāmarrā.

The same Sāmarrā body and opaque cream glaze, which has turned pinkish grey during burial, is seen in the ware painted with bold foliage, Cufic characters, wreaths, and other designs in a dark cobalt blue (fig. 10) and occasionally in green. The blue designs are sometimes supplemented by splashes of green (fig. 11) and manganese brown; and there are fragments with monochrome glazes including a dark purplish blue, an opaque blue of lighter and more lavender shade, a dark bottle-green, emerald green, and yellow. Some of the green and yellow fragments are remarkably thin and finely potted. Again, the green and yellow glazes are used for wall tiles. Of the two pieces illustrated, one is a shallow bowl painted in blue with a representation of a fire altar, and the other a rare vase with a blue wreath-design and splashes of green.

Some of the monochromes should perhaps be included among the imitations of Chinese pottery, which form such an interesting group. The importance of the finds of Chinese stoneware and porcelain at Sāmarrā is discussed in another Guide.[1] They include white porcelain, and yellowish white stoneware, celadon porcelain, and stoneware with green and yellow, besides splashed and mottled, glazes. One of the splashed fragments has a design engraved with a point under the glaze. All these types except the celadon[2] are represented by imitations of Near-Eastern make, so close in many

FIG. 10. Blue-painted bowl. 9th century.

cases that they can only be distinguished from the Chinese originals by examining the body material. The Sāmarrā imitations are on the soft Sāmarrā body, which is light buff in colour and easily powdered under the knife. The Chinese wares resist the knife and, in the case of the porcelain, have a white body.

Among the Sāmarrā imitations are ewers with short, straight spout and handle with a palmette in relief below it, and other

[1] *Guide to the Pottery and Porcelain of the Far East*, pp. 15, 22, &c. Examples are exhibited in the Window-case, Bay IV.

[2] The celadon was freely imitated in Egypt and Persia, but at a later date.

PLATE III

FIG. 11. VASE: NINTH CENTURY

FIG. 12. Part of a ewer from Sāmarrā.

FIG. 13. Basin found in fragments at Sāmarrā.

ornament consisting of pads of stamped relief in pure Tʿang style
(fig. 12). These pieces have a pale streaky yellow glaze with
splashes of brown. Others are foliate bowls with plain white
glaze copying Chinese originals even to the finish of the base.
Another large group has splashed and dappled glaze of white or
yellowish white colour with green and manganese brown markings:
a few rare pieces have a yellow glaze splashed with manganese.
Often these pieces are decorated with etched designs, and in this
case they generally have a red body with a white slip coating through
which the design is incised with a fine point (fig. 4). Fragments
of this kind of ware found among the remains of kilns at Kura
on the outskirts of Sāmarrā are apparently of slightly later date
than the ninth century: but there were specimens, older in style,
found on the palace sites which are undoubtedly of the old
Sāmarrā period.[1]

BRAHMINABAD

One of the virtues of the Sāmarrā discoveries is that they
enable us to appreciate the importance of other finds which are
not so precisely dated by their history. Thus the pottery found
in considerable quantity in the Mohammedan strata at Susa has
now been studied in the light of the Sāmarrā finds by Raymond
Koechlin[2], and it is seen to comprise practically all the Sāmarrā
types (Table-case in Bay XXVII). Practically all of them again
have been dug up at Rhages, near Teheran; some of them have
been found in the neighbourhood of Rakka in Syria, and most of
them in the waste-heaps at Fosṭāṭ in Egypt. Again there is
a small but highly interesting group of potsherds in the same
Table-case which were found in the ruins of Brahminabad,[3]
about fifty miles north-east of Hyderabad in Sind. They include:
(1) Lustred ware of Sāmarrā and Fosṭāṭ types, some with buff and
some with red body, among which is a remarkable little tray in
the form of a dove painted inside with a hare in greenish brown
lustre and outside with 'net' patterns. It has Cufic characters in
relief under the base (apparently the initials of a name) and in
lustre on the tail (fig. 14). (2) A fragment of thin reddish buff
pottery with fine floral scroll outlined in relief and glazed brown
and green (fig. 15). (3) Part of a bowl with Sāmarrā body and
opaque white glaze imitating Chinese. (4) Wares of the Samarkand

---

[1] An interesting pot of this splashed ware in Chinese style was found in
Susa with coins of the tenth century. See *Mission Archéologique de Perse*,
Tome xix, *Les Céramiques Musulmanes de Suse*, par Raymond Koechlin,
Pl. XV, No. 112.

[2] *Op. cit.*

[3] In 1854 by A. F. Bellasis and C. M. Richardson: published by the
former at the Bombay Education Society's Press in 1856: some of them
were figured by Wallis, *Persian Ceramic Art*, Appendix, Pl. VI.

PLATE IV

FIGS. 14–18. FRAGMENTS FROM BRAHMINABAD

type (p. 21) with low flat base covered with glaze, and red body dressed with white slip and covered with a yellowish white or green lead glaze. Under the glaze are designs outlined in manganese brown and filled in with washes (fig. 16), stripes or dots of ochreous red (fig. 17): painted in black: incised with a point (fig. 18): or *graffiato*. With these were pieces of Chinese porcelain and stoneware some of which are exactly like those found at Sāmarrā.[1]

Existing accounts of Brahminabad are meagre and much involved with legend; but it is certain that the city was flourishing at the beginning of the Hijra (A.D. 622) and it is believed with good reason that it was destroyed about the year 1020. Legend regards its destruction, probably by an earthquake, as a divine punishment for the iniquities of its king Diloo Raee. The same legend tells of one Chota, a brother of this king, who went to Bagdad and being a Mohammedan married an Arab woman, whom he brought back with a number of Arab settlers to Sind.

In view of the Sāmarrā types of pottery found there this reference to intercourse with Bagdad is interesting; but the Moslems invaded Sind and partially conquered it in the eighth century, and it is probable that our pottery found its way to Brahminabad at least a century before the time of Chota. On the other hand fig. 14 has much in common with the early lustred pottery found at Fosṭāṭ, and the possibility of its having been imported from Egypt must be taken into account.

It is obvious from these finds in India that Near-Eastern pottery as well as Chinese porcelain were articles of commerce in early Mohammedan times; and that the fragility of the goods did not prevent their being carried great distances. This is further confirmed by the story that the lustred tiles in the mosque of Sidi Ocba in Kairuan, Tunis, were brought from Bagdad in the year 894, and this story in turn is borne out by the nature of the tiles in question, which is precisely that of the Sāmarrā lustre ware. Again, lustred fragments and unglazed pottery with enamelled decoration in Sāmarrā style have been found at the Qal'a of the Benī Hammād (Algiers), which was built in the early years of the eleventh century: and lustred pottery hardly distinguishable from that found at Brahminabad has been unearthed on the site of Medīnat az-Zahrā near Cordova in Spain, a city which was built in 936/7 and destroyed in 1010. Finally, a fragment of lustre ware of the Sāmarrā type is among

---

[1] The Chinese pieces include: (1) fragments of a large dish with foliate rim, porcelain with yellowish white glaze; (2) porcellanous ware with closely crackled yellowish white glaze; (3) ware with cream white glaze of Ting type; (4) celadon of the 'Northern Celadon' type; (5) stoneware with painted designs in brown under a watery celadon glaze; (6) similar ware with splashes of ferruginous brown. See *Transactions of the Oriental Ceramic Society*, 1928/30.

the potsherds collected in the neighbourhood of Samarkand which are in the Victoria and Albert Museum.

It may be that there were potteries in North Africa and Spain founded by Near-Eastern potters to cater for the local needs; but there is no reason why the finer kinds of pottery should not have been distributed from some centre or centres in the Near East such as Rhages, Bagdad,[1] or Fosṭāṭ. It can hardly have been from Sāmarrā, where the industry could only have had a few years' existence: but perhaps it was from Bagdad or some other Mesopotamian centre, though we have no evidence as yet to confirm this suggestion. On the other hand, Rhages (see p. 15) is regarded by some authorities as the fountain-head, and certainly Rhages has been prolific in the pottery remains of all kinds and all periods down to the thirteenth century. But we can only pose the question. At present there is no means of deciding it. The same uncertainty exists as to the time and place where lustred pottery was first produced. Rhages, Mesopotamia, and Egypt are the three principal claimants, and each has its determined supporters. But the arguments on all sides rest chiefly on stylistic grounds, and there is room here for endless difference of opinion. The spade of the excavator is the only weapon which is likely to decide the contest. Meanwhile the only established facts are that the art of lustre decoration was fully developed in the period when Sāmarrā flourished, that is the ninth century, and that the Sāmarrā type of lustre ware continued to be made in the tenth and eleventh centuries, as shown by its presence at Medīnat az-Zahrā and the Qalʿa of the Benī Hammād.

The one dated twelfth-century specimen of lustre ware (fig. 25) is of the later Rhages type and would seem to show that the transition from the early Sāmarrā type had taken place some time before 1180. Literary references are so scarce that it is worth recording that the twelfth-century poet Farīd likens a pottery dish to a golden dish, a comparison which can hardly refer to anything but lustre ware.

It would appear, then, that there was no break in the continuity of the lustre manufacture in Persia from the ninth century to the thirteenth; and after that we have plenty of evidence of its vitality as far as the seventeenth century.

EGYPT

Fosṭāṭ, south of Cairo, was built by ʿAmr after the Arab conquest of Egypt on the ruins of a more ancient city. In 1168

[1] Karabacek ('Zur Muslimischen Keramik,' *Monatschrift für den Orient*, Dec. 1884, No. 12), summarizing the results of his literary researches, mentions as famous for pottery about the ninth century, Ḥimṣ in Syria, and al-Kūfa, al-Baṣra, and above all Bagdad in Irak.

it was destroyed and given over to fire: partially rebuilt, it was pillaged in 1252 by the Mamelukes, after which disaster it never completely revived. What remains of it is known as Old Cairo. The ruined sites of Fosṭāṭ are covered with rubbish mounds, and the whole area has been found to be full of fragments of pottery made at all periods from the Arab conquest onwards. Large collections have been formed of these fragments, and they are deeply interesting in the variety of types which they illustrate ; but the circumstances in which most of them were found unfortunately do not greatly assist the chronological classification of them.

Egypt was famed for its artistic pottery in dynastic times and under the Roman Empire, and it is unlikely that the traditions of the ceramic art have ever been completely forgotten there ; but there is little evidence of its vitality in the three centuries preceding the Arab conquest. The Copts were the craftsmen of Egypt during this period, and what little we know of Coptic pottery is not very inspiring. It is certain, however, that there was a great revival in the Moslem period, perhaps assisted by potters from Persia and Mesopotamia, as happened at a later time when the Mamelukes imported artists and workmen from Persia and Syria. At any rate much pottery of the best Sāmarrā types and evidently of the ninth and tenth centuries has been found at Fosṭāṭ, besides refined wares with designs which obviously belong to the art of the Fatimid period (952–1171). We have, moreover, the evidence of the Persian traveller Nāṣir i Khusrau (1035–42) that pottery of every kind was made at Miṣr (Cairo), that they made among other things bowls, cups, dishes, and other articles of a translucent ware, and that they used colours which changed according to the position in which the vessels were held as on a (silk) stuff called *bougalemoun*.[1]

Dr. Fouquet[2] published a useful study of a large series of fragments from Fosṭāṭ and the late Aly Bey Bahgat[3] more recently made an attempt to classify the principal types.

The British Museum possesses a considerable series of Fosṭāṭ fragments, of which a number are exhibited in the drawers of Table-case H. They date, however, mostly from the thirteenth century onwards, and the early types are sparsely represented. Of the Sāmarrā types, of which Fosṭāṭ has produced a great number, there are a small piece of the thin buff ware with relief designs and yellow glaze coated with lustre, and several fragments painted in olive brown and yellow lustre, but none with mixed

---

[1] It has been suggested that this refers not to pottery but to another product of Egypt, semi-opaque glass with lustred decoration.

[2] *Contribution à l'Étude de la Céramique Orientale*, Cairo, 1900.

[3] *Fouilles d'Al Foustat*, Paris, 1921 ; and, with M. Félix Massoul, *La Céramique Musulmane de l'Égypte*, Cairo, 1930.

lustres of red, green, and golden yellow tints, There are, however, several good specimens of golden lustred wares in Fatimid style including one with the signature of Sa'd (fig. 6), an important eleventh-century decorator. Some of the monochrome pieces,

FIG. 19. Jar of Egyptian pottery. 12th century.

with blue, green, or yellow glaze, have incised designs (fig. 19) which indicate a similar date.[1] Of the *graffiato* wares (pp. 24–31), of which Fouquet describes a few early examples, the collection possesses a large series of Mameluke date but none earlier.

Other early specimens from Egypt include a beautiful fragment from Kōm Washīm, north-east of the Fayūm, with thin, white body,

[1] A waster of this kind of ware with yellow glaze shows that it is of local make.

which has weathered to a buff colour, and relief designs of an animal with a vine branch in its mouth, filled in with green and manganese glazes in a yellow ground (fig. 5). Site evidence indicates that this piece is not later than the ninth century. There is also a fragment of the Samarkand type with painted designs on a slip-faced red ware, which was found at El-'Azami; and a few pieces with splashed glazes of T'ang type on a Sāmarrā body which were found at Oxyrrhynchos. And in Case C, Bay XXVII, there are a few lustred specimens of the early Fosṭāṭ type, two candlesticks and a shallow bowl. But, as already stated, the bulk of our Egyptian fragments belong to later periods, and they will be discussed in another place.

FIG. 1. Amphora of coarse-grained reddish buff pottery with blue glaze which is decayed and iridescent. Said to have been found at Rakka.
About the 3rd century A.D.   H. 11·7 in.

FIG. 2. Part of a pannikin of reddish buff pottery with moulded reliefs and a green lead glaze. Excavated at Sāmarrā. L. 4·25 in.

FIG. 3. Part of a dish of reddish buff pottery with moulded relief ornament and yellow lead glaze covered with brilliant lustre. Excavated at Sāmarrā.   L. 1·75 in.

FIG. 4. Part of a bowl of reddish buff pottery with incised decoration (cable border, &c.) under a creamy lead glaze which is splashed and mottled with yellow, green, and manganese brown. Excavated at Sāmarrā.   L. 6·4 in.

FIG. 5. Part of a flat-bottomed dish of fine white pottery with design in raised outlines and filled with green and manganese brown glazes in a yellow-glazed ground. Found at Kōm Washīm, north-east of the Fayūm.
Probably 9th century.   L. 5·3 in.

FIG. 6. Part of a dish of sandy white ware with clear silicious glaze of a yellowish tone: decorated in olive brown lustre with ornamental details etched out with a fine point. On the reverse is part of the signature of Sa'd.
Fosṭāṭ, 11th century.   L.3·1 in.

FIG. 7. Basin of pale buff pottery with opaque creamy white glaze decorated in green and yellow lustre, which in places passes into red.
Sāmarrā type.   D. 10·5 in.

FIG. 8. Part of a rectangular tile of buff pottery with opaque white glaze decorated with a floral wreath in a marbled ground in green, yellow, and dull red lustre with dark brown outlines. Excavated at Sāmarrā.   L. 9 in.
The complete design, a cock within a wreath, can be reconstructed from Sarre, *Die Keramik von Samarra*, Pl. 22.

FIG. 9. Part of a square tile of similar ware with flower design in dark brown. Excavated at Sāmarrā.   L. 6·3 in.

The design, part of a floral scroll, is reconstructed in Sarre, *Die Keramik von Samarra*, p. 53.

FIG. 10. Shallow bowl with curved sides and sharply everted rim. Fine buff pottery with opaque white glaze painted in blue with a fire altar and three conventional flames.
Sāmarrā type.   D. 8·3 in.

FIG. 11. Vase with three handles and a pair of pierced uprights on which the cover was hinged. Buff pottery with opaque greyish white glaze, painted with a wreath in blue and splashed on the handles and shoulders with green.
Sāmarrā type.   H. 9·4 in.

FIG. 12. Part of a ewer of buff pottery with yellow glaze and a splash of brown: below the spout is a shield-shaped pad with indistinct stamped ornament. Excavated at Sāmarrā.   D. 4·7 in.

FIG. 13. Basin of buff pottery with creamy white glaze streaked with broad splashes of yellow and green.   D. 13·75 in.
Restored from fragments excavated at Sāmarrā.

FIG. 14. Tray in the form of a dove, of fine reddish pottery with opaque creamy white glaze painted in olive brown lustre. Inside the bowl is a hare, the spaces filled with a dotted pattern. On the reverse is a pattern of lines and dots suggesting network. Excavated at Brahminabad.   L. 5·3 in.

The decoration of this piece and the character of the ware and lustre compare closely with fragments found at Fosṭāṭ. See Aly Bey Bahgat and Félix Massoul, *La Céramique Musulmane de l'Égypte*, Pl. IV, fig. 1.

FIG. 15. Fragment of reddish buff pottery with raised designs and green lead glaze. Excavated at Brahminabad.   L. 2 in.

FIG. 16. Bottom of a bowl of fine red pottery with white slip dressing and trellis design painted in manganese brown, red, and yellow under a creamy white glaze. The base is shallow and concave and partially glazed. Excavated at Brahminabad.   D. 2 in.

FIG. 17. Part of a bowl of red pottery with white slip dressing and geometrical design painted in brown, red, and yellow under a creamy white glaze. Excavated at Brahminabad.   L. 3·4 in.

FIG. 18. Fragment of red pottery with white slip dressing decorated with an incised band of ornamental Cufic characters in a hatched ground: the glaze is pale green. Excavated at Brahminabad.
L. 1·5 in.

FIG. 19. Jar (*albarello*) of light red pottery with interlacing designs incised under a leaf-green lead glaze.
Found in Upper Egypt. 12th century.   H. 6·6 in.

PLATE V

FIG. 20. DISH: TWELFTH CENTURY

RHAGES

About five miles south-east of Teheran are the ruins of Rhages (Rayy), a city of great antiquity and once among the largest and most famous in the East. It was ruthlessly sacked by the Mongols in 1220 and, though some effort was made to revive it, its place was taken by the neighbouring Teheran and Veramin, and after the fourteenth century it was virtually abandoned. The ruins of

FIG. 21. Part of a bowl with 'transparencies'. 12th century.

Rhages have long been a happy hunting-ground for treasure seekers, and great quantities of pottery have been excavated in the usual haphazard fashion, pieced together, and placed on the market. A good series of fragments from Rhages was presented to the Museum by F. Du Cane Godman in 1891, but they belong chiefly to the second period of our classification.

Earlier deposits excavated by French enterprise have produced a great variety of the older Mohammedan wares including all the types found at Sāmarrā and Susa, and in addition the Northern Persian *graffiato* ware. How much of this pottery was made at Rhages it is for the moment impossible to say. The excavations, such as they are, have been made primarily for profit, and it is likely enough that persons working in this spirit would take no account of kiln wasters which might, if preserved,

have thrown light on local manufacture. Only two such wasters
have been published[1], and they belong to the later period; but
they show at any rate that pottery was made at Rhages and,
as we are told that there is abundance of good material in the
neighbourhood, it is probable enough that Rhages was itself a great
manufacturing centre.

Of the early types of pottery reputed to have been found at
Rhages the Museum has several specimens, but there is no

Fig. 22. Cup with carved ornament. Perhaps 10th century.

evidence to connect them with Rhages itself. Consequently
the blue and white and the lustred ware and other members of
the Sāmarrā group have been included in the Sāmarrā section,
and the *graffiato* wares are treated separately (p. 24). There
remains the fine, white, almost porcellanous ware, which is
decorated with incised or deeply carved patterns. In this we see
an extension of the *graffiato* technique to a white ware; and the
designs, which are often very beautiful, are sometimes filled in
with coloured glazes—blue, green, yellow, and manganese purple
(fig. 20). It has been noted that this kind of ware was also found

[1] By Henry Wallis, *Persian Ceramic Art*, 1891, Pl. XXIX, figs. 7 and 8.
They are in the Table-case, Bay XXVII.

and perhaps made at Rakka. Another variety of this ware has part of the ornament cut right through the wall of the piece and filled in with clear glaze so as to form transparencies. There is a beautiful ewer of this type in the Louvre[1] dated tenth to twelfth century, and the remnant of a bowl in Standard-case I, though perhaps a little later, illustrates the fairy-like beauty of this kind of decoration (fig. 21).

The same class of ware with incised designs (fig. 23), with or without transparencies, is found with a lovely, clear blue glaze.

FIG. 23. Bowl with blue glaze and 'transparencies'. 12th century.

Fragments of this kind, too, are reported to have been unearthed at Rhages. Fig. 24, a dish decorated with a boldly carved design of an eagle in scrolls under a delicious turquoise blue glaze, may be as early as the twelfth century, though it has touches of the red enamel used on the Rhages polychrome pottery (see p. 44). Other Rhages types which are of great variety and beauty will be discussed with the next period; but reference must again be made here to the fragmentary bottle (fig. 25), with decoration in lustre and a date equivalent to 1179/80 of our era. The early lustred wares reputed to have been found at Rhages are of the Sāmarrā type with fine buff earthenware body. This important specimen has the sandy white body which is usual in the later Rhages wares, and the quality of the golden lustre with ruby reflections connects it closely with the later lustre wares of Rhages.

[1] Illustrated by Gaston Migeon, *Manuel d'Art Musulman*, vol. ii, fig. 318.

C

Fig. 25 and 25 a. Lustred bottle. Dated A.D. 1179/80.

PLATE VI

FIG. 24. RHAGES DISH: TWELFTH CENTURY

RAKKA

Another town which must have been of considerable importance
in the days of Sāmarrā is Rakka, which is situated on the
Euphrates about a hundred miles east of Aleppo. To-day it
is a village which marks the site of several ruined cities, Nicephor-
ium, which was probably founded by Alexander, and Callinicum,
a fortress visited by Julian, seized and sacked by Chosroes,
rebuilt by Justinian, and taken by the Mohammedan invaders in
633. The position was strengthened by another fortified city
named Rāfikah (the Comrade) which was built by Manṣūr in
772; and either here or in the old city, which was called Rakka,
the famous Caliph Hārūn ar-Rashīd built himself a residence.
In the days of Yākūt the geographer (c. 1225) the older Rakka
had already disappeared. The twin city was sacked by the
Mongols in 1259, and in 1321 Abu al-Fidā wrote that the whole
place was reduced to uninhabited ruins. Gertrude Bell,[1] who
describes a visit to the site, tells us that 'the whole of the two
areas of ruin are strewn with potsherds of the Mohammedan
period, and over the greater part of the walled city the ground
is honeycombed with irregular holes and trenches, the excavations
of peasants in search for the now celebrated Rakka ware. . . .
In some instances the original factories and kilns have been
brought to light'.

Quantities of Rakka pottery excavated in this haphazard
fashion have passed through the hands of dealers in Aleppo and
found their way into Western collections, but all trace has been
lost of the circumstances of the finds. We only know what the
history of the site tells us, namely that this pottery is anterior
to 1321 and that it was probably made on the spot. Professors
Sarre and Herzfeld visited the ruins in 1907/8 and, though they
were prevented from making proper excavations, they examined
the site, and Professor Sarre[2] has published an important study
of the results of their investigations.

The typical Rakka ware is a loose sandy material, greyish
white in colour, lightly fired, and friable. It is, in fact, a variety
of that sandy whitish pottery which from about the twelfth
century onwards became the standard pottery of the Near East.
This body is covered with a silicious glaze which, though naturally
clear and transparent, is sometimes rendered opaque and cloudy by
colouring matter of greenish blue or turquoise tint. The soil of
Rakka has acted as a strong solvent of this glaze; and most of
the buried specimens are heavily encrusted with gold and silver
iridescence, due to decay.

[1] See Gertrude Bell, *Amurath to Amurath*, pp. 53–60.
Keramik der Euphrat- und Tigris-Gebiet, Berlin, 1921.

The earliest Rakka specimens have the plain green or turquoise glazes. This glaze can be traced back at least to Parthian times, and individual examples are hard to date. Next come the obviously Islamic wares, painted in black under a pale peacock blue glaze (fig. 26). This evidently became the stock production of Rakka, but it is not clear when it was first made. Certainly the style of many specimens would suggest a date not later than the eleventh or twelfth century. A fragment of a beautiful dish of this kind of ware and possibly of Syrian make is shown in the Table-case in Bay XXVII. The dish was embedded in the wall of the church of Santa Cecilia in Pisa, which was founded A.D. 1103. The fragment was obtained by the late Mr. Drury Fortnum. Lustre painting must have been practised, too, about this time, to judge from some rectangular tiles in the Kaiser Friedrich Museum, Berlin, which Professor Sarre attributes to the tenth or eleventh century.

The lustre which was freely used at Rakka from the twelfth century onwards is of a characteristic kind and of a dark olive brown colour which is rarely seen elsewhere. A typical example, but probably of thirteenth-century date, is the vase (fig. 27) with ornamental Naskhi characters in high relief painted with broad washes of brown lustre with a semé of dots in the spaces. Another vase with similar shape and reliefs but with a blue glaze is seen in the Standard-case. The Rakka lustre is sometimes combined with blue as on the vase and lamp in Case C, Bay XXVII; and another type of painted ware common to Rakka and the Syrian potteries and to Egypt has decoration in blue and black under a clear glaze.[1] All these types occur among the fragments and wasters found at Rakka, though it is probable that many of our specimens are later than the twelfth century. M. de Lorey, of the French Institute of Moslem Archaeology and Art at Damascus, also found at Rakka fragments of the beautiful ware illustrated by fig. 20. It is a fine white ware of sandy texture with boldly carved designs touched with blue and in some cases with other colours such as green, yellow, and manganese. The same explorer found fragments of the *graffiato* ware of Northern Persian type (see p. 25), and mottled wares in the Chinese T'ang style.

Some of the finest wares of the Syrian group are said to come from the ruins of Ruṣāfa, the Byzantine Sergiopolis, in the neighbourhood of Rakka. A large basin with wide flat rim in the Kaiser Friedrich Museum[2] is attributed to Ruṣāfa on the strength

[1] A rather crude pottery painted in blue and black under the glaze appears among the fragments in the Victoria and Albert Museum which were found at Samarkand and presumably date from the ninth or tenth century.

[2] Berliner Museen, *Berichte aus den Preussischen Kunstsammlungen*, Heft 1, 1927, *Drei Meisterwerke Syrischer Keramik*, by Professor F. Sarre.

PLATE VII

Fɪɢ. 26. RAKKA DISH: TWELFTH OR THIRTEENTH CENTURY

PLATE VIII

FIG. 27. RAKKA VASE: THIRTEENTH CENTURY

PLATE IX

FIG. 28. RAKKA STAND: THIRTEENTH CENTURY

PLATE X

FIG. 29. RUṢĀFA BOWL: TWELFTH CENTURY

of fragments excavated on the site. It has a striking design of a small peacock whose radiating feathers spread over the sides and rim of the dish; and it is painted in lustre and underglaze colours. Another basin in the same collection is painted in blue, green, black, and a thick dull red which is the forerunner of the sixteenth-century Turkish red,[1] with a horseman attacked by a lion. These pieces are assigned to the twelfth century. They and other presumed Ruṣāfa specimens are distinguished by the fine, free draughtsmanship of their designs, which compares favourably with that of any other Near-Eastern pottery.

To this class belongs a rare bowl (fig. 29) with a figure of a man brandishing a scimitar painted in blue and brown with touches of green and the thick red mentioned above; and perhaps a bowl in the Van den Bergh gift (Pillar-case) with a spirited drawing of a goose (?) in blue and brown.

SAMARKAND

Allusion has been already made to Samarkand, which we gather was noted for pottery at more than one period of its existence. In the suburb of Āfrāsiyāb, which was a place of importance in the tenth century under the Sāmānid dynasty, much pottery has been found. Most of it is in Russia, but a good selection of fragments was secured by the Victoria and Albert Museum in 1898, and there are a few stray pieces in various Western collections. The characteristic ware from this quarter has a red earthenware body which is dressed with white or brown slip and painted in coloured slips—white, red, brown, black, yellow, and greenish yellow—under a transparent lead glaze of yellowish tone. The designs consist largely of ornamental Cufic characters and scrolls with diapers of dots in the spaces. Besides these there are pieces with incised designs and mottled green and yellow glaze in Chinese T'ang style; rough *graffiato* wares spotted with green: and finer ware painted in bluish green, or blue and black under the glaze. Among the Victoria and Albert fragments is one piece of lustred pottery of the Sāmarrā type.

That the bulk of these fragments should belong to the ninth or tenth century seems clear from the Sāmarrā types found there, from the style of the Cufic lettering, and from the fact that the large, slip-decorated group has close affinities with the fragments found at Brahminabad (p. 8). Talbot Rice illustrates, on Plates III and VI of his *Byzantine Glazed Pottery*, fragments found at Constantinople which are closely akin in style of decoration to the Samarkand ware.

[1] Pottery with similarly coloured decoration, including the red, has been found at Miletus: probably an importation from Syria. The red is derived from Armenian bole and is applied in the form of a clay slip: see p. 87.

A specimen of the typical Samarkand pottery is illustrated by fig. 30, a basin of red ware with white slip dressing and rough designs including Cufic characters in black and red slip under a yellowish lead glaze. The base is low, slightly concave, and trimmed at the edge, features which one remarks on the Brah-

FIG. 30. Samarkand basin. 10th century.

minabad fragments ; and there is the usual dotted ornament filling the spaces.

Another bowl in Case E of Bay XXVIII, though not identical in finish, perhaps belongs to the same family. It is painted in manganese, yellow, orange, and white slips, with bands of formal ornament and dotted borders.

A third specimen, a small jar with yellow glaze streaked with manganese purple in T'ang style, exactly resembles a piece found at Samarkand. Here, however, the body is of the fine buff material which is such a constant feature of Sāmarrā pottery, and it may be merely one of the kinds of ware imported, like the lustred fragments in the Victoria and Albert Museum, into Samarkand.

It may be noted here, though outside the limits of the early period, that Clavijo (in the narrative of his embassy to the Court of Timur, A.D. 1403–6) states that in 1402 Timur carried off from Damascus to Samarkand weavers of silk, men who made bows, glass, and earthenware, 'so that of these articles Samarkand produces the best in the world'. Further, there is modern pottery made in the neighbourhood of Samarkand which keeps alive the traditions of the old slip-painted ware.

FIG. 20. Dish of sandy white pottery with transparent silicious glaze which is crazed in places and stained. The central designs are incised and coloured with blue, turquoise green, and aubergine purple. The human-headed bird is variously known as the 'anḳā or sīmurgh. Said to have been found at Rhages.
12th century. D. 16·75 in.
See coloured postcard C 198.

FIG. 21. Part of a bowl of sandy white pottery with creamy white silicious glaze. Inside is a band of raised Cufic lettering (a religious formula), and below this a frieze of horsemen in foliage scrolls finely carved, with the background pierced and filled with glaze.
12th century. D. 8·2 in.

FIG. 22. Cup of similar ware with carved band of 'honeysuckle' scrolls and vertical fluting.
Perhaps 10th century. H. 4 in.

FIG. 23. Bowl of similar ware with incised and semi-transparent designs under a pale blue glaze.
Rhages (?). 12th century. D. 7·7 in.

FIG. 24. Dish of similar ware with carved design of an eagle and foliage scrolls under a turquoise glaze. Details painted in dry red pigment, with touches of gilding.
Rhages (?). 12th century. D. 15 in.
See coloured postcard C 199.

FIG. 25. Part of a bottle. Sandy white ware with cream-white, tin glaze painted in golden brown lustre with ruby reflections. The inscription contains the date 575 A.H.[1] (= A.D. 1179/80).
Rhages (?). H. 5·5 in.

FIG. 25a. Bottom of 25.

FIG. 26. Dish of sandy, buff white ware painted in black under a turquoise blue glaze with ornamental Naskhi lettering, the spaces filled with foliage scrolls and dots.
Rakka. 12th or 13th century. D. 10·1 in.
See coloured postcard C 208.

---

[1] Other authorities have read this date as 578 A.H. (= A.D. 1182/3).

FIG. 27. Vase of sandy, buff white ware with silicious glaze and formal Naskhi characters in relief painted in brown lustre.
Rakka. 13th century.   H. 13·5 in.

FIG. 28. Stand for bowls (?). Sandy whitish pottery with ornament moulded in relief, covered with a creamy white glaze and painted in brown lustre. On each side is a 'tree of life' between two confronted griffins among scrolls.
Rakka. 13th century.   L. 11·2 in.

FIG. 29. Bowl of sandy white ware painted in blue, brown, and green with touches of thick red under a silicious glaze.
Ruṣāfa. 12th century.   H. 8·5 in.

FIG. 30. Basin of reddish buff pottery with dressing of white slip and designs in red slip and dark brown under a glaze of warm creamy tint. On the sides are formal Cufic characters.
Samarkand. 10th century.   D. 10·7 in.

GRAFFIATO WARE

The common features of this ware,[1] which is distributed all over the Near East, are a red or reddish buff earthenware body, a coating of white clay or slip, and a transparent lead glaze which has a faint yellowish tone when it is not actually coloured green or purplish brown by means of metallic oxides. The glaze and slip are applied with care on the decorated surfaces, but on the exterior of bowls and dishes they are often represented only by a few random drops or splashes. The decoration is formed by incising through the white slip coat so as to expose the red body beneath, either in fine lines traced with a stylus or by scraping away wide areas of slip around the pattern, which is left standing in white in a red ground. The former decoration we may distinguish as incised and the latter as *champlevé*.[2] It should be added that painting in liquid clays, or slips, is sometimes used to supplement both these kinds of decoration and even in some cases as a substitute for them.

Incising, carving, and painting in slips are all simple and natural pottery processes, and it is hardly possible to say when or where they were first used on this type of ware in the Near East. Few of the specimens found in Egypt, Ephesus, Salonika, the Crimea, or in the region of Constantinople can be said with certainty to be earlier than the tenth or eleventh century.[3] The

[1] A few years ago the name Gabri was given to this kind of pottery in the belief that it was made by the fire-worshipping (Gabri) inhabitants of Persia, before the establishment of Islam. Gabri is still used as a trade term for this and other early Persian wares.

[2] This French term, which we have adopted for want of a better one in English, is normally applied to enamelled metal-work, in which the field of the design is cut away so as to form cavities for the enamel.

[3] The Egyptian specimens quoted by Dr. Fouquet (*Contribution à l'Étude*

incised type was found at Sāmarrā and Susa, but not the *champlevé*. Both are seen among the Brahminabad fragments and both are found in some quantity at Rhages and on other sites in Northern Persia. Indeed it is from Northern Persia that most of our *champlevé* specimens have come. Various provenances are habitually given by traders—Rhages, Veramin, Zanjān, Hamadān, Āmul—but so far no kiln-site evidence has been produced to show where the ware was made. There is little doubt that it was found in the earliest strata at Rhages, and it is likely enough to have been made there. Much is also stated to have come from Zanjān, but there is reason (short of actual proof) for supposing that the Zanjān ware was not made there but at Yasukend, near Sinneh in Ardalān.[1] This is the typical Persian *champlevé* ware with boldly cut decoration of birds, animals, human figures, and Cufic inscriptions in floral scrolls. The designs stand out in yellowish white against a warm reddish brown ground, and they are frequently variegated with splashes of green and purplish brown. Sometimes the green extends over the whole surface. The rendering of the animals and birds is often spirited and artistic, that of the human form is usually coarse and grotesque; but perhaps the most attractive specimens are those with bands of ornamental Cufic characters, while the floral scrolls, which are almost Gothic in feeling, often have great beauty. The warm colouring of the yellows and reddish browns is pleasing; but the ware on the whole must be regarded as a kind of peasant pottery, ranking with the slip-wares of seventeenth-century Europe, and lacking the refinement of the buff faïence of Sāmarrā and of the white ware of Rhages and Rakka.

The character of the ware is seen in the specimens in Case E, Bay XXVIII, and in the Table-case. The bowl with the camel (fig. 31) and that with a lion are typical specimens of 'Yasukend' ware. They are of red ware, with small base slightly concave, and their colouring is yellowish white and reddish brown relieved by splashes of green.

The ewer (fig. 32) is decorated in good style with Cufic characters which Dr. Flury reads as *li-ṣā-ḥi-bi-hi* (to its owner), and which he dates from the style of the script to the eleventh century. This is about the period to which we may ascribe the other *champlevé* specimens in the Collection with animal and human designs and foliage scrolls, because of their general similarity in style to the inscribed specimens. We have at present no other means of dating them more exactly, and they doubtless cover

de la Céramique Orientale, p. 125) are of a different type, viz. that with decoration in raised outlines as found at Sāmarrā and Susa, and therefore irrelevant.
[1] I am indebted for this information to Mr. Rowland Read.

a considerable range of years, perhaps from the tenth to the twelfth century.

If indeed this class of pottery ceased to be made in Persia in the thirteenth century, and it is by no means certain that it did, it is curious that it was apparently only just reaching its full development in Egypt at this time, under the rule of the Mame- lukes. The Egyptian *graffiato* ware is distinguished by the free use

FIG. 31. *Graffiato* bowl. 10th to 12th century.

of armorial bearings, and it is evident from an inscribed fragment that it was largely used in the households of the great.[1] It is richly decorated with panels of inscription, scrolls, cable patterns, interlacings, &c., the general effect being often very like that of the incrusted 'Mosul' metal-work: the designs usually extend to the exterior of bowls, which is not the case with the Persian wares; and free use is made of green and manganese to reinforce the red-brown and yellow which are the basic colours of the ware (fig. 33). The ware itself is generally dark red (sometimes a lighter red) and the cream and yellow tints are obtained by washes of white slip under the lead glaze.

[1] Fouquet, *op. cit.*, p. 132, describes a fragment with inscription 'made for the kitchen of Mr. ——'.

PLATE XI

FIG. 32. GRAFFIATO EWER:
ELEVENTH OR TWELFTH CENTURY

The manufacture of this ware apparently continued in Egypt through the fourteenth and fifteenth centuries; and somewhat similar pottery was probably made at the same time in Cyprus (see p. 29) and in other places along the Eastern Mediterranean. To return to Northern Persia, there are other kinds of *graffiato* slip-ware besides this bold *champlevé* type. There is, for instance, a finely incised pottery with very little of the background scraped away, and having neat small designs which give something of

FIG. 33. Egyptian *graffiato* bowl. 14th century.

the effect of the stamped ornament of book-bindings (fig. 34), while another kind has designs merely incised in thin lines. There is again a cruder kind of ware (fig. 35) with designs of grotesquely rendered animals, birds, and scrolls under a yellowish glaze stained and spotted with green, in general effect somewhat resembling poker-work. Specimens of this ware have been found at Rhages, Zanjān, and Āmul.

Āmul is credited with yet another type with strongly incised birds and beasts coloured with yellow and ochreous red in addition to the more usual green and manganese. The background is sometimes filled in with rather angular scrolls which are more suggestive of coral branches than foliage, sometimes with circles and groups of dots. Other specimens have the main designs painted instead of incised, or again there are pieces with a combination of painted and incised ornament. They are certainly Northern Persian types, but it is only hearsay evidence which connects them with Āmul, a city on the southern shores of the Caspian and on the route between Northern Persia and Samarkand. Fig. 36 illustrates an interesting bowl which, though not of the *graffiato* class, is mentioned here because it is reputed to be of Āmul make. It has a reddish buff body dressed with black clay and painted in white with a griffin and four swans in a ground dotted in Samarkand style.

Fig. 34. *Graffiato* bowl. 10th to 12th century.

The *graffiato* types are fully represented among the Byzantine pottery described by Talbot Rice.[1] The finer *champlevé*, such as fig. 34, is closely paralleled by Constantinople specimens illustrated on Plate XIII of his book and ascribed to the eleventh or twelfth century; and the bold *champlevé* class by a beautiful cup (Plate I of the same book), which, however, is not older than the thirteenth century.

Fragments of *graffiato* wares are found in many places on the shores of the Eastern Mediterranean, e.g. Smyrna, Ephesus, Miletus, Salonika, Athens, and the Museum has a considerable series of cups and bowls excavated in Cyprus at Claudia, Larnaka,

[1] *Byzantine Glazed Pottery*, University Press, Oxford, 1930.

and elsewhere (Table-case H). This Cyprus pottery, though constructed on familiar lines, has a distinctive character. The body is a light red or reddish buff pottery which has the usual wash of white slip on the interior and sometimes on the exterior as well. The ornament is rather roughly executed with a stylus

Fig. 35. Dish with incised designs. 10th to 12th century.

which cuts through the white slip into the red body, and it is covered with the usual yellowish lead glaze variegated with splashes of green and brownish yellow. In general tone the ware is lighter than the normal Egyptian *graffiato* ;[1] the potting is less finished, and feet of bowls and cups are thicker and more splayed. Further, the designs used differ in one important feature from the Egyptian types, namely in the frequent occurrence of the human

[1] The fine bowl, with an ostrich displayed inside it (fig. 37), though found in Cairo, has all the characteristics of the Cyprus group.

form in the decoration. An exceptional bowl in Table-case H is decorated with whorls of white slip under a green glaze. The shapes, too, of the Cyprus wares are peculiar, especially those of goblets (fig. 38) and bowls.

There is no evidence to show whether this ware was made on the spot or imported from Egypt or elsewhere; but its individual character certainly points to local manufacture.

Fig. 38. Goblet of Cyprus ware. 13th or 14th century.

The pottery found during J. T. Wood's excavations at Ephesus (1863–74) includes a variety of types—*graffiato* wares of the incised and *champlevé* kinds, slip decorated wares, unglazed water vessels with reliefs, and blue and white silicious-glazed pottery of fifteenth-century Anatolian type. How much was of local make it is difficult to say; but moulds for forming the raised ornament on the water vessels, and tripod supports or spurs for the *graffiato* ware prove that these two sorts at any rate were made on the spot. The *graffiato* ware[1] has a red body with the usual white slip dressing and a lead glaze coloured in places

[1] Wallis, *Persian Ceramic Art*, 1891, illustrates a number of specimens in Pls. III to VI of the Appendix.

PLATE XII

Fig. 36. SLIP-PAINTED BOWL: TENTH CENTURY

PLATE XIII

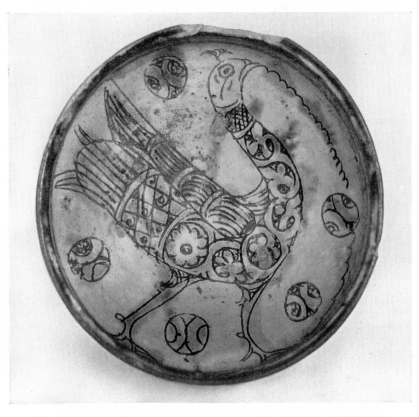

FIG. 37. BOWL OF CYPRUS (?) WARE: THIRTEENTH CENTURY

with green, yellow, and manganese. It approximates closely to the Mameluke pottery of Egypt in general appearance, but there are a few fragments which may date from the eleventh or twelfth century. The water vessels appear to be of later date, and they are very similar to those found at Miletus[1] and ascribed by Professor Sarre to the fourteenth and fifteenth centuries.

FIG. 39. Bowl. ? Syrian. 13th or 14th century.

The important bowl (fig. 39) with a mounted archer among foliage scrolls is closely analogous in technique to the Cyprus wares. It is reputed to have been found in Syria, near Aleppo, with other specimens. Possibly it is a Syrian variety of the Cyprus type. The decorative design and the colouring are reminiscent of some of the Northern Persian pottery; and it may be regarded as a link between the eleventh-century Persian wares and the late Byzantine *graffiato* pottery of Cyprus.

[1] In the Kaiser Friedrich Museum, Berlin. See F. Sarre, 'Seljuk and early Osmanli Pottery of Miletus', *Transactions of the Oriental Ceramic Society*, 1930/31, Pl. VII.

UNGLAZED POTTERY

Unglazed, porous pottery has always been in request in Eastern climates for its water-cooling properties, and the specimens, whole and fragmentary, of this ware from various sites form a considerable group ranging over many centuries. They stand apart from the other kinds of pottery in their nature and to some extent in the type of decoration which their nature has demanded, and it will be convenient to treat them separately.

The ware is generally a fine-grained, buff pottery, soft enough to scratch easily with a knife. It is used chiefly for water vessels —cisterns, jugs, bottles, and cups; and its decoration is usually formed by incising with a point, carving (in openwork or otherwise) with a knife, stamping, or applying relief designs in various ways, e.g. by strips of clay, by liquid clay or slip (*barbotine*) trailed on from a pipette, or by pressing in hollow moulds. Incised designs and trailed or applied reliefs are to be seen on vessels which belong to the earliest years of Islam, possibly to still earlier periods; and the same *barbotine* technique survives in such pieces as the neck of a large cistern (fig. 40) at the end of the Table-case in Bay XXVII and the fragment of a flask beside it. The mounted archer among scrolls on the latter piece reflects Sassanian tradition, but from analogy with other specimens it seems probable that neither of these pieces is older than the eleventh century.

The same *barbotine* technique is observed on Sāmarrā pottery of the ninth century, but the bulk of the unglazed fragments from this important site are decorated with incised geometrical designs and with small stamped reliefs of deer, birds, horsemen, and occasionally potters' signatures in small round medallions. A few are painted in unfired pigments like the plaster wall-decoration which was found on the same site. It is something of a surprise to find that as early as the ninth century this unglazed ware was occasionally decorated with thick, glassy enamels, tinted blue, green, and yellow with metallic oxides and trailed or painted on in geometric designs, foliage scrolls, or Cufic lettering. The thick, upstanding lines of enamel suggest that the process was a development of the *barbotine* technique. Specimens of this type have been found at Sāmarrā, Susa, and the Qal'a of the Benī Hammād.[1]

There are other specimens of unglazed pottery in the Collection. One, fig. 41, is a jug with cable border, a band of ornamental

---

[1] See F. Sarre, *Die Keramik von Samarra*, Pls. VII and VIII; Raymond Koechlin, *Les Céramiques Musulmanes de Suse au Musée du Louvre*, Pl. XIII, 107; G. Marçais, *Les Poteries et Faïences de la Qal'a des Benî Hammâd*. Examples from the last site are exhibited in the Musée des Arts Décoratifs in Paris.

Cufic lettering, and hexagons containing fantastic animal designs
(a prowling tiger, a griffin, confronted hares, a bird, &c.) with
scrolls in the spaces. It is assigned by Dr. Flury on epigraphic
grounds to the end of the eleventh century. Another has a relief
band with four medallions of peacocks separated by peacocks and
a spread-eagle design. Jugs of this kind were made at all periods.

Fig. 40. Neck of a water jar. 12th century.

There is a specimen in the Louvre[1] dated 1216: and numerous
fragments of them have been found in Egypt, where water vessels
of somewhat similar character are made to this day. Their
necks are generally fitted with a more or less artistically perforated
diaphragm intended to keep flies and other impurities from the
water.
    The early enamelled water vessels of Sāmarrā and Susa have

---

[1] G. Migeon, *L'Orient Musulman*, Pl. X. In the Kaiser Friedrich Museum,
Berlin, is a silver jug with relief bands which suggest that our pottery
ornament is in many cases derived from metal-work. This jug is dated
thirteenth century. See Kühnel, *Islamische Kleinkunst*, fig. 125.

more sophisticated descendants in the thirteenth century, such
as fig. 42, a cup of unglazed pottery painted in blue enamel
with two rows of figure subjects. It has been suggested that the
figures with peaked caps in the lower row may be dervishes, but
the seated figures in the upper row are those of the Rhages

FIG. 41. Water jug. About 1100.

polychrome and lustred wares of the early thirteenth century.
Indeed, it is probable that this piece itself was made at Rhages.

A later edition of these porous vessels is seen in the little
group of jugs at the West end of Table-case H. They are made
of fine-grained pottery sometimes pale red, sometimes greyish
white: they are lightly fired, and generally have a slight polish on
the surface. They are ornamented in various ways. Some have
rosettes in applied relief, supplemented by incised and pricked
designs of formal flowers, cable borders, &c.; and parts of this
ornament are coloured with a brown slip and sometimes also

heightened with oil gilding (fig. 43). Others have rows of small stamps, floral or otherwise; and others have painted ornament in a red pigment which may perhaps be only a medium for oil gilding. Such gilding would readily wear off, though in many cases it still remains. Cypress trees and growing plants rendered in this pigment recall in style the designs on the seventeenth-century Persian lustre ware (p. 66). Pierced patterns are common on the bases of these jugs, and inside the necks are tiers of elaborately

FIG. 42. Water jug. 13th century.

pierced diaphragms in the form of sunflowers, rosettes, &c., and sometimes with passages of Arabic script. At the base of the handle there is often an inscribed stamp which in some cases has been read as giving the name of the potter. In several others, however, the stamp reads *ṭīn makhtūm* (=*terra sigillata*), indicating that they were made of a special clay which was believed to have medicinal properties.[1] All the Museum specimens are

[1] In the same Table-case are a cup and saucer with a stamp declaring them to be *terra sigillata*. An explanatory note is attached—'Cup and saucer of *terra sigillata*, a peculiar silicious earth from the volcanic island of Lemnos believed to possess medical qualities. It is dug up on the 6th August with religious ceremonies in the presence of the Governor, and the parcels are sealed—hence the name. The Sultan has some and the rest is sold—the cup

reputed to have been found in Sicily, but it is certain that they
were made by Mohammedan potters, and the seventeenth century
is indicated as their date.

There is no doubt that the manufacture of this porous pottery

FIG. 43. Water jug. 'Sicilian' ware. 17th century.

was as widespread in the East as it is perennial. Quantities of it
have been found in Mesopotamia; and Professor Sarre speaks of

and saucer have been moulded by hand.' The medicinal clay of Lemnos
was known to the Greeks and Romans in classical times. It was taken
internally as well as made into pots. In the sixteenth century its vogue was
revived in Europe, and the Turks exploited the beds at Lemnos. Similar
material, however, was found in Germany, France, Italy, and elsewhere,
and was stamped and sold as *terra sigillata*.

a large trade in it at Mosul in modern times. Writing in the seventeenth century, Chardin tells us that very porous clay was found at Kūm 'of which the inhabitants make unglazed water-cooling bottles and drinking vessels, which are sent to the surrounding parts of Persia'. But it is certain that there were many other centres of manufacture besides Kūm and Mosul.

Reference should be made here to the pointed oval 'grenade' in Case F, Bay XXVIII, which is of unglazed pottery with stamped and incised ornament. It is much harder-fired than the water vessels which we have been discussing, for, whatever its intention, it was not meant to be porous. Objects of this kind more or less artistically decorated and sometimes glazed have been found in many places in the East. The present specimen came from Bulandshahr, NW. Provinces, India. Many suggestions have been made as to their purpose—such as for bombs, bottles for carrying quicksilver or holy water, lamps, counterweights, finials, &c.; but the most probable is that they were used for holding inflammable material to be hurled at the enemy in battle.

Fig. 31. Bowl of red pottery with dressing of white slip on the interior and *champlevé* design of a camel in foliage scrolls: creamy white glaze with patches of green.
10th to 12th century. D. 6·35 in.

Fig. 32. Ewer with remains of handle and spout. Red pottery with dressing of white slip and *champlevé* designs under a yellowish lead glaze with a few splashes of manganese brown. On the neck are three panels with ornamental Cufic characters which have been read *li-ṣā-ḥi-bi-hi* (= to its owner). Said to have come from Khorāsān.
11th or 12th century. H. 7·8 in.

Fig. 33. Bowl of dark red pottery with dressing of white slip and incised designs coloured ochreous red, green, and purplish brown under a creamy lead glaze. Inside are radiating panels with a lozenge-shaped heraldic device alternating with Naskhi inscriptions. From Fosṭāṭ. 14th century. D. 9·2 in.

Fig. 34. Bowl of buff red pottery with dressing of white slip and incised decoration under a creamy lead glaze.
10th to 12th century. D. 6·7 in.

Fig. 35. Dish of red pottery with dressing of white slip and incised designs stained and spotted with green, under a creamy lead glaze.
10th to 12th century. D. 13·45 in.

Fig. 36. Bowl of buff pottery with dressing of black slip and designs painted in white slip.
Āmul (?). 10th century. D. 6·7 in.

Fig. 37. Bowl of light red pottery with dressing of white slip inside and incised design of an ostrich under a creamy lead glaze. Obtained in Cairo: but probably Cyprus ware.
13th century. D. 6·8 in.

FIG. 38. Goblet of light red ware with dressing of white slip and incised designs splashed with yellow and brown under a creamy lead glaze.
Said to have been found under a Byzantine church in Cyprus.
13th or 14th century.   H. 4·8 in.

FIG. 39. Bowl of light red pottery with dressing of white slip on the exterior and incised designs coloured with green, brownish yellow, and manganese under a creamy lead glaze. Said to have been found near Aleppo.
13th or 14th century.   D. 10·2 in.

FIG. 40. Neck of a large water jar. Buff pottery decorated with incised ornament, applied reliefs and drops and traceries of clay.
Probably Mesopotamian. 12th century.   H. 13·1 in.

FIG. 41. Jug of light buff pottery decorated with bands of stamped ornament.
Probably Mesopotamian. About 1100.   H. 6·5 in.

FIG. 42. Jug of thin buff pottery with designs in thick blue enamel. The figures with peaked caps in the lower medallions are perhaps intended to be dervishes.
13th century. (Van den Bergh Collection.)   H. 4·2 in.

FIG. 43. Cooling jug of buff white pottery with incised and applied ornaments, some of which are washed with brown slip and gilt. Below the handle is a stamp which reads *ṭīn makhtūm* (= *terra sigillata*).
'Sicilian.' 17th century.   H. 8·6 in.

PERIOD II

(From A.D. 1200 to 1400)

RHAGES

OF the second period into which we have divided our material the thirteenth and fourteenth centuries were a time of great ceramic splendour. In spite of the devastation inflicted by the Mongols the potters' art seems to have flourished. The fragments obtained by F. D. Godman at Rhages and given to the Museum in 1891 reveal wares of the utmost refinement and in great variety. It is probable that most of these were made before 1220, about which time Rhages was crushed by a double disaster, first the destruction following bitter religious strife and then the massacre of 'some 700,000' of its inhabitants by the Mongols: but the temporary revival of the city in the reign of Ghāzān Khān (1295–1304) may account for some of them.

Unfortunately the casual search for pottery in the ruins of Rhages has been carried on solely for the benefit of the antique trade; and in these circumstances it is not surprising that such ungainly objects as kiln-wasters should have been neglected. Consequently we are without proof that the bulk of the pottery found in such quantities on the site is of local make. All the kiln-site evidence that we have up to date are two bottoms of bowls (Table-case, Bay XXVII) to which the triangular kiln-supports still adhere.[1] They are of sandy white pottery with deep blue glaze, and one of them is painted with lustre designs. These apparently insignificant objects are of the utmost importance.

Fig. 44. Rhages bowl. 13th century.

They prove that Rhages was not merely an emporium but a centre of the ceramic industry, and they show that two of the most characteristic features of the Persian pottery of our second period, a lovely deep blue glaze and golden lustre, belong to the Rhages potteries. Doubtless many waste pieces of other kinds of pottery have been spurned by the treasure hunters at Rhages and may yet be recovered by searchers who understand their archaeological value. But at least we can feel that there is nothing illogical in supposing that many of the other types of pottery found there were made on the spot. An examination of the body material and potting of these two wasters helps us in some measure to identify other Rhages specimens, but not so much as might be expected; for these bowls are rather roughly finished, and the sandy white ware of Rhages does not differ greatly from the material used all over the Near East at this period. Compared with that of Rakka it is a little whiter, harder, and of slightly

[1] See H. Wallis, *Persian Ceramic Art*, 1891, Pl. XXIX, figs. 7 and 8.

Fig. 45. Rhages lustred bowl. A.D. 1209.

Fig. 45A. Side view of the same.

finer grain: the Rakka body is less pure in colour and more loose
and powdery in texture. The Sulṭānābād body is generally
greyer. But the differences where they exist are very subtle,
and sometimes one can see nothing to distinguish the body
material of the several kinds of ware. Nor again does the glaze

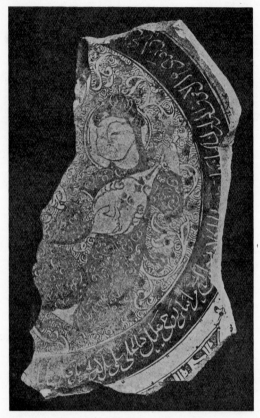

Fig. 46. Rhages lustred ware. Early 13th century.

tell us much; for practically all the Near-Eastern wares of this
period have a colourless silicious glaze, which is either clear and
transparent or rendered creamy and opaque by the use of slip
or tin,[1] or again tinted blue, turquoise, or green by mineral
oxides.

[1] The opacity is usually put down to the presence of tin; but a chemical
analysis of a fragment of the ware showed only a very small proportion of
this ingredient.

But whether or not we accept the Rhages finds as of Rhages
make, it will be convenient to discuss under one heading the
different types found on this prolific site.

(1) *Lustred wares.* Compared with the early 'Sāmarrā lustres'
the typical lustre of the second period is simple. It is almost

Fig. 47. Rhages lustred *albarello*. 13th century.

uniformly golden brown with a tendency to ruby reflections:
occasionally it appears to sink into the glaze, forming a deep
reddish stain. The Rhages lustre is usually applied over an
opaque creamy glaze; but it is also used on dark blue and pale
lavender blue glazes; and sometimes the sides of a bowl are
partitioned by bands of lustred blue alternating with bands of
lustred cream (fig. 44).

There is no clear line of division between our first and second

periods, and doubtless many of the Rhages types overstep the
artificial boundary which we have set at 1200. The lustred
pottery certainly does, for fig. 25, a characteristic specimen,
is dated 1179/80. It has all the features of our second period
wares and the subjects of the decoration are quite characteristic
and characteristically treated, namely dumpy figures seated

FIG. 48. Rhages lustred dish. 13th century.

among scrolls: bands of hares and dogs reserved in a ground of
lustre: etched inscriptions and foliage scrolls.

The positive and negative methods of painting—i.e. expressing
the design in lustre and leaving it reserved in a lustre ground—
and etching inscriptions and minor ornament out of a wash of
lustre are seen in fig. 45, a bowl with inscription dated A.D. 1209.
On the side of this bowl is a splash of blue which might be taken
as accidental if it did not occur on so many other specimens.
The most likely explanation is that, blue being a lucky colour
this splash was intended to bring good luck to the owner. Blue,

however, came to play a much more prominent part in the combination, especially on the tilework (p. 96). The best Rhages lustre painting is illustrated by the large fragment with a finely drawn figure of a lute player (fig. 46), which may be compared in style with the famous Shīrīn dish in the Eumorfopoulos Collection[1] which is dated 1210. Other examples in Standard-case I have

FIG. 49. Rhages lustred basin. 13th century.

bands of horsemen separated by formal trees, and seated figures (fig. 47), which are obviously related to the designs of the 'Rhages polychrome' (see below).

(2) 'Rhages polychrome.' Just as the lustre pigment was applied to the finished ware and fired at a low temperature in a special kiln, so the colours used in this type of decoration were painted on the glaze and fixed by firing in an enameller's kiln or 'muffle'. They took the form of vitrifiable enamels, or coloured glass, finely powdered and liquefied and painted on with

[1] *Catalogue,* vol. vi, Pl. LXVI.

a brush. The palette was a large one, including a blue which sinks into the glaze, and a glossy blue which stands out on the glaze, turquoise, brownish red, manganese purple, green, brick red, black, and white, to which must be added leaf gilding; most of these enamels have a rather dry, mat appearance. The ground for this decoration was usually a cream glaze, as in the case of the lustre

FIG. 50. Rhages polychrome bowl. 13th century.

ware, but dark blue and light turquoise were also used with singularly rich effect, and occasionally the unglazed surface of buff earthenware water-vessels was enriched with Rhages enamels. The brushwork as a rule was careful and refined; and the style of painting and colouring as well as the choice of subject often recall the work of the Court miniaturists of the early part of the thirteenth century. Indeed it is thought that the artists who decorated the beautiful Persian manuscripts may have assisted in the decoration of this pottery. The motives are not unlike those of the lustred wares: figures seated cup in hand, kings and queens

and their attendants: subjects from romance, such as Bahrām
Gūr hunting: pairs of horsemen separated by formal trees:
'sphinxes', birds, and animals in the spaces (figs. 50 and 51). The
fragmentary bowl (fig. 52) is painted with the delicacy of a minia-
ture, and there are pieces of bowls in the Table-case, Bay XXVII,
which show this type of decoration at its best. Other specimens

FIG. 51. Rhages polychrome bowl. 13th century.

have formal designs of arabesque scrolls and foliage and geometrical
patterns; and in some instances parts of the decoration are built
up in relief (fig. 54) or embossed with openwork medallions of
unglazed clay which is gilt and enamelled.

A very effective variety has the splendid dark blue Persian
glaze enamelled with formal designs in white and dull red, with
gilding added (figs. 55 and 56). Some of the most beautiful mosque
tiles belong to this family; and there are tiles and plaques with
similar pigmentation on turquoise blue glaze in combination with
glazed or unglazed reliefs.

FIG. 52. Rhages polychrome bowl. 13th century.

FIG. 53. Rhages polychrome bowl. 13th century.

FIG. 56. Rhages polychrome bowl. 13th century.

FIG. 57. Rhages or Sulṭānābād. 13th century.

PLATE XIV

FIG. 54. RHAGES BOWL: THIRTEENTH CENTURY

PLATE XV

FIG. 55. RHAGES DISH: THIRTEENTH CENTURY

FIG. 58. Rhages bowl. 13th century.

FIG. 59. Rhages bowl. 13th century.

E

So much of this polychrome pottery has been found at Rhages and so little elsewhere that it has been named 'Rhages polychrome', implying that it was a manufacture peculiar to that city. A few pieces, however, were found in the diggings at Khar, a site which produced many of the best types of classical Persian ware, and also at Veramin; but both places are near Teheran and therefore within easy reach of Rhages. Isolated specimens found farther afield, as at Miletus, &c., were probably also imported from Rhages.

Other Rhages types include pottery with dark blue (fig 57) or opaque turquoise blue glaze over carved designs or moulded reliefs: but Sulṭānābād and Rakka are rival claimants in the case of these

Fig. 60. Rhages ware. 13th century.

kinds of ware. Again, among the Rhages fragments there are specimens of a highly effective decoration in black and turquoise. Here the white ground of the pottery is covered with a layer of black slip: the design is cut through this layer into the white, or conversely the design is left in black and the surrounding areas are scraped clear down to the white: and over all is a pale turquoise blue glaze. Fig. 58 will illustrate this explanation. Bands of similar black slip with incised inscriptions are combined with bold foliage scrolls and grasses, with cusped ends, painted in brown-black on a white ground in another group, which is sufficiently akin to these to be assigned to Rhages (fig. 59). There is a bowl of this class dated 1211.[1] The foliage scrolls and grasses in their turn would suggest a Rhages origin for such pieces as the two jugs in the Van den Bergh Collection (Pillar-cases). A tiny fragment (fig. 60) shows that transparencies (see p. 17) were probably used on Rhages pottery of this period.

VERAMIN

It is not known whether Veramin, a city a few miles south of Teheran, which rose to importance after the desolation of Rhages, was a centre of ceramic manufacture or not. But its ruins have yielded a quantity of broken pottery of the finest Persian types; and some of the most beautiful lustred tiles known

[1] E. Kühnel, 'Datierte persische Fayencen', *Jahrbuch der asiatischen Kunst*, Leipzig, 1924.

FIG. 61. Bowl, probably Rhages. 13th century.

FIG. 61A. Side view of fig. 61.

have come from the mosque which was built about 1262. The tiles are described in another section (p. 96). For reasons which are not very satisfying the name of Veramin has been connected with a much less sophisticated pottery which is supposed to have been made there in the fourteenth century. It has a red earthen-

FIG. 62. Fosṭāṭ ware. 13th century.

FIG. 64. Bowl: 'Miletus' ware. 14th century.

ware body, like that of the early *graffiato* wares, covered with a white slip and painted with blue, green, and manganese purple under a clear glaze. The decoration is often of a formal, geometrical kind, curiously like some of the pottery found at Paterna in Spain. Sometimes it takes a more artistic form, as in fig. 63, a dish with a spirited drawing of a bird in the centre of a blossom-shaped medallion, painted in blue with manganese outlines and powdered with dots of manganese brown.

PLATE XVI

FIG. 63. VERAMIN (?) DISH: FOURTEENTH CENTURY

Ware of the same general type found in the excavations at Miletus[1] is described by Professor Sarre; and it may be that the whole group belongs to Asia Minor rather than to Persia. An attractive bowl (fig. 64) with a radiating design of formal plants in dark blue and manganese belongs to the Miletus group.

SULṬĀNĀBĀD

Fine pottery has been found in considerable quantity and variety in excavations at Sulṭānābād. At any rate it is so stated by the traders who placed the wares on the Western market. But the case of Sulṭānābād is typical of the obscurity which beclouds so many of our attempts to classify Persian pottery. There is more than one Sulṭānābād in Persia, but the locality persistently associated with these finds is a town situated about half-way between Kūm and Hamadān. This place does not appear on a map of the year 1200, and the earliest date on a specimen of reputed Sulṭānābād ware is 1227, which leaves a quarter of a century for the growth of the town, a possible but not very adequate margin. But, in any case, assuming that the pottery in question was found at this Sulṭānābād, there is no further evidence that it was made there; and it will be well to regard the name Sulṭānābād for the present merely as a convenient label.

It is certain at any rate that the site of these finds was rich in beautiful pottery, and many of the best specimens had the distinction, rare among Persian pots, of being preserved entire. This was due, it is said, to their being buried inside large crocks, while the more ordinary pieces were as usual found broken in the ground. Among the 'Sulṭānābād wares' are several which have common characteristics with the Rhages pottery, such as painting in lustre, painting in blue and lustre,[2] and decoration in low relief under dark blue, turquoise, and green glazes (figs. 65 to 67). But there is one type which has a strongly individual character and which is as characteristic of Sulṭānābād as the 'Rhages polychrome' is of Rhages.

Fig. 68 is a good example of this ware. It has a loose, sandy body of greyish white colour and a clear silicious glaze. The decoration is executed according to two schemes. In the one case the ground is dressed with white slip and on this the designs are outlined and shaded in brown, the background being filled in with blue. In the other the white slip is used to build up the design in low relief against the natural grey ground, which is

---

[1] See p. 31 and *Transactions of the Oriental Ceramic Society*, 1930/31.
[2] The ewer with bird's head on its neck (Postcard C 205) is said to have been found at Sulṭānābād.

hatched with brown pencilling. The medallion in the bottom of fig. 68 and the floral scrolls on the exterior are executed according to the former scheme; the figures inside and the inscription outside according to the latter. Both schemes produce very attractive results, whether used separately or in combination. Two shades of blue are used, a full dark colour and a paler tint verging on turquoise.

FIG. 66. Bottle. 13th century.

The motives most commonly employed by the decorators of this ware are animals, birds, and more rarely human figures, framed by flowers and foliage. The bodies of the animals and the robes of the human figures are usually covered with a semé of dots. It is significant that Chinese influence is very marked in the ornament of this ware. The human figures (as in fig. 68) are often of Mongol type and the Chinese lotus is conspicuous among the flowers. In other examples the phoenix and dragon actually occur. It is indeed certain that much, if not all of this ware, was made after the period of Mongol occupation.[1] An inscribed

[1] Hūlāgū Khān is said to have transplanted 1,000 Chinese artificers and their families to Persia.

PLATE XVII

FIG. 65   FIG. 67

BOTTLE AND EWER: THIRTEENTH CENTURY

PLATE XVIII

F IG. 68. SULṬĀNĀBĀD BOWL: LATE THIRTEENTH CENTURY

PLATE XIX

Fig. 69. SULṬĀNĀBĀD BOWL: THIRTEENTH CENTURY

PLATE XX

Fig. 70. SULṬĀNĀBĀD DISH: THIRTEENTH CENTURY

specimen in the Kelekian Collection has the date 1278 ;[1] and two lustred specimens reputed to be from Sulṭānābād in the same Collection are dated 1227 and 1270 respectively.[2]

The technique of this Sulṭānābād decoration may be conveniently studied on the jug in Case D of Bay XXVIII, ornamented with a cheetah hunting deer in the usual foliage background. The surface of this piece is so perished that the glaze has peeled off the greater part of it, and gives us as it were a peep behind the scenes, showing clearly how the raised ornament was modelled in the wet clay in low relief.

The pleasing quality of the grey Sulṭānābād clay as a background for reliefs and painting is illustrated by two jugs in the same Case. Other good examples are in Standard-case I, a dish with a bird in the centre and another with a hare or long-eared deer, both from Teheran, and a dish with a peacock (fig. 70). The fine *albarello* with three birds in foliage comes from Cyprus. It may perhaps be of Egyptian make, for, as observed on p. 59, pottery of this kind was also made at Fosṭāṭ. A handsome bowl with radiating panels of storks in foliage in the Van den Bergh Collection shows the use of the two shades of blue (fig. 69).

There are also specimens of the blue- and brown-painted wares of Syrian type and of wares painted in black under a turquoise glaze which are assigned to Sulṭānābād. The former appear in a series of dishes and shallow bowls in Table-case H which seem to be all of similar make. Some of these have passages of the typical Sulṭānābād decoration, while others have the blue and brown painted designs. A dish of the latter type comes from excavations near Teheran (fig. 71). To this class again belong two bowls in Standard-case I, West side. They are widemouthed with rounded sides contracted at the lip, which has a flat rim. This class of bowl is seen again in Case D of Bay XXVIII, in specimens which are reputed to have come from Sulṭānābād, and it would seem that this was a favourite Sulṭānābād shape (fig. 68).

There are many other types of early Persian pottery which are not connected with any particular locality, and there are many other probable centres of manufacture. Hamadān, Kūm, Meshed, Natinz, Kāshān are names associated for various reasons with lustre ware, either because specimens have been found there or because lustred tiles have come from their public buildings. But there is no evidence at present to show that any special type is peculiar to any one of these localities.[3] The manufacture of

---

[1] *Catalogue of the Kelekian Collection of Persian and Analogous Potteries*, Pl. LXXII.   [2] *Ibid.*, Pls. XXXIX and LI.

[3] Karabacek, *Zur Islamischen Keramik*, names a number of towns as directly or indirectly mentioned in literature as producing pottery—Kāshān, Ḥimṣ (Syria), Kūfa, Baṣra, Bagdad, Sīrāf, Kirmān, Ispahan,

pottery seems to have been very general throughout Persia, and
the material and technique to have varied little in the different
districts.

Thus if we take the most frequent types of this second period
such as pottery with (1) moulded reliefs or openwork covered
with dark blue, opaque turquoise blue, green, or white glazes,

Fig. 71. Dish found near Teheran. 13th century.

(2) ornament painted in lustre with or without blue, (3) ornament
painted in black under a clear turquoise blue, green glaze or
colourless glaze, (4) ornament painted in blue and brown under
a clear glaze, we find that it is practically impossible to differen-
tiate the lustre wares if we except the peculiar olive brown lustre
of Rakka. With regard to the ware with glazed reliefs we have
described one type which is found at Rakka (p. 20), and there,
too, were undoubtedly made such pieces as the four-legged stand

Shīrāz, Ṭūs, Nīshāpūr, and Kūm. A thirteenth-century work mentions
Ispahan as specially noted for the skill of her potters. The ruins of Saveh
(between Rhages and Hamadān) have lately produced large quantities of
pottery of various kinds.

(fig 28): but similar wares are claimed for Rhages and Sulṭānābād, and similar reliefs appear on tiles in various parts of Persia. The splendid vases in the Freer and Havemeyer Collections in America dated respectively 1239 and 1283 show that this type of ware belongs to our period, but its place of manufacture is a matter of conjecture.

The blue and turquoise glazes were also used as plain mono-chromes without any relief; but monochrome of this type is

Fig. 72. 'Waster' from Damascus kiln-site.

not common except where it is obviously based on Chinese models, such as the celadon green, the lavender blue of the Chün ware, and the plain white.

As to the third and fourth categories, specimens belonging to these have been found all over Persia, though probably this technique was nowhere used more freely than in Syria and in Egypt in the thirteenth and fourteenth centuries. Rakka,[1] Damascus, and Fosṭāṭ have given us proof of local manufacture in the convincing form of wasters; and the ware was found in quantity in the ruins of Baalbek.

A waster from a kiln-site near Damascus (fig. 72) shows a sandy and very friable body, similar to that used at Rakka, painted in

[1] A jug in Case D of Bay XXVIII, obviously a waste specimen, comes from Rakka. It is decorated with a frieze of hounds and scrolls in black under a beautiful turquoise blue glaze.

a vivid dark blue, a brownish black, and a thin turquoise blue under a transparent silicious glaze which is much crazed and has a greyish cast. It is a roughly made ware, but in the style of the Syrian and Egyptian pottery. Adhering to it are remains of kiln-supports. Comparison with this piece suggests that the goblet-shaped bowl in the Pillar-case, Bay XXVI, middle, is a

FIG. 73. Probably Syrian. 13th or 14th century.

superior specimen of this ware: but it is hardly possible to formulate any rules for distinguishing the wares of this class which were made in Persia, in Syria, or in Egypt.

EGYPT

The ruins of Fosṭāṭ, so prolific in ceramic remains, and the earlier types of pottery found there have been discussed on p. 12. But there is a great quantity of potsherds collected in the Fosṭāṭ rubbish-mounds which belongs to our second period. Doubtless some of these are imported, for they include Rhages and Sulṭānābād types[1] and even Spanish lustred ware: but the bulk of them were made on the spot and there is ample kiln-site evidence of large local manufactures. The local ware has either a red pottery body or a sandy, greyish white body of the general Near-Eastern type.

Of the four groups into which the Fosṭāṭ fragments may be

FIG. 74. Egyptian or Syrian. 14th century.

conveniently divided the *graffiato* wares have been discussed on p. 26. The lustred specimens, though including a number of the early 'Sāmarrā' and Fatimid types, may in the main be assigned to our second period. They are, however, hardly to be distinguished from the lustre ware of Persia and Syria. The bottom of a fine *albarello* (fig. 74) with fluted sides in Case C of Bay XXVII has lustre decoration over a dark blue glaze. This piece

[1] See, however, Aly Bey Bahgat and F. Massoul, *op. cit.*, p. 73, where evidence is produced to show that a decoration of 'Sulṭānābād' type, with parts of the designs in low relief, was used by an Egyptian potter in the middle of the fourteenth century.

belongs to that sumptuous type of pottery which is represented by two large vases in the Victoria and Albert Museum[1] and by another belonging to the Comtesse de Béhague.[2] The last-mentioned has an inscription reading 'made for Asad of Alexandretta (or Alexandria) by Yūsuf of Damascus'; while one of the former is inscribed with the name of Mu'ayyad al-Manṣūr, Sultan of Egypt; and they should be of fourteenth-century date.

A third group comprises the mass of pottery painted with designs in blue and black, singly or together, under a clear glaze. This ware is generally of the sandy, greyish white variety, and the bottoms of bowls are often signed with the mark of the decorator. This type ranges over a long period, lasting certainly as late as the sixteenth century. The earlier specimens closely resemble the Syrian wares of the thirteenth and fourteenth centuries (i.e. those found at Rakka, Damascus, Baalbek, &c.), and some of them are actually signed ash-Shāmī (=the Syrian). The later specimens, especially those painted in blue alone, derive their ornament from Chinese porcelain, of which large quantities were imported into Egypt.

Among the Fosṭāṭ fragments in Table-case H there is a series of bowl-bases in drawer 8 inscribed with potters' signatures[3] including those of ash-Shāmī, Ghā'ibī, al-Shāʿir, Siwaz, Ghazal, at-Taurizī, al-Hormuzī, besides a number of abbreviations. The commonest name, Ghā'ibī, simply means stranger, and this is sometimes qualified by a further description such as ash-Shāmī, the Syrian. Evidently there were many foreign potters settled in Egypt, for the names at-Taurizī and al-Hormuzī indicate natives of Tauris and Hormuz: and it is certain that the decoration in blue and black, though perhaps of Syrian origin, was freely used in Egypt. This is proved not only by Egyptian signatures such as al-Miṣrī (the man of Miṣr or Cairo), but by numerous wasters found at Fosṭāṭ. The painting of these wares is often of a very attractive character and finely executed, a typical scheme for the interior of bowls being radiating panels such as those in fig. 75. Painting in black under a turquoise glaze is also common to Egypt and Syria.

A fourth large group consists of monochromes. Besides the bluish green and turquoise glazes which are found everywhere in the Near East, numerous single-colour glazes were used by the Egyptian potters. Some of these clearly aim at reproducing the glazes of the Chinese Sung and Yüan wares, particularly that of

---

[1] H. Wallis, *Early Persian Lustre Ware*, Pl. VII.

[2] Migeon, *Manuel d'Art Musulman*, fig. 363.

[3] With the exception of a serpentine scrawl on one Egyptian piece and two dashes and a dot on another, the only marks on the pottery of our two first periods in the Collection consist of potters' signatures: and these signatures hardly occur except on wares of Egyptian origin.

PLATE XXI

Fig. 75. EGYPTIAN BOWL: FOURTEENTH CENTURY

PLATE XXII

FIG. 76. EGYPTIAN VASE: FOURTEENTH CENTURY

the sea-green 'celadon' porcelain of Chekiang, which was traded freely in the Near East from the ninth century onwards. The Egyptian celadons achieve considerable success in the imitation of this glaze colour and they make free use of the Chinese ornamental motives, such as fishes (fig. 77), or floral rosettes in relief on the bottoms of bowls, or incised floral scrolls; but they are readily distinguished from their Chinese models by the softer

Fig. 77. Egyptian dish. 15th century.

and more earthy body material. The collection of Fosṭāṭ fragments includes numerous specimens of these celadons, as well as pieces of the Chinese originals: and there are complete examples in Case F, Bay XXVIII. Another Chinese glaze deliberately copied is the lavender grey of the Chün ware, with or without splashes of purple.

Other Egyptian monochromes with transparent blue, leaf green, yellow, and manganese purple glazes have been mentioned among the wares of the first period. These were doubtless freely used in the second period also, and as a rule they have incised ornament under the glaze. A red body is not unusual in the case of these Egyptian monochromes, as may be seen in a waster from Fosṭāṭ which has a leaf-green glaze.

Fig. 44. Bowl of sandy white ware with dressing of white slip and a clear glaze. Inside are radiating compartments alternately blue, turquoise and cream white, painted in brown lustre. Inside is a Naskhi inscription in lustre on a blue ground.
Rhages. 13th century. (Van den Bergh Collection.)   D. 7·5 in.

Fig. 45. Bowl of sandy white ware with opaque creamy glaze painted in lustre: a patch of blue on the side within. The inscription on the inner border contains the date *rabi'-al-auwal*, A.H. 606 (= 3rd of September to 3rd of October A.D. 1209).
Rhages.   D. 11·3 in.

Fig. 46. Part of a dish of sandy white ware with opaque creamy glaze painted in golden brown lustre with ruby reflections, with a figure of a lute-player and a band of Naskhi inscription.
Rhages, about 1200.   L. 9·75 in.

Fig. 47. Jar (*albarello*) of similar ware painted in golden brown lustre with ruby reflections, and with touches of blue.
Rhages. 13th century.   H. 9·2 in.

Fig. 48. Dish of similar ware painted in golden brown lustre with ruby reflections, and with touches of blue: blue glaze outside.
Rhages. 13th century.   D. 10·4 in.

Fig. 49. Basin of similar ware painted in golden brown lustre with ruby reflections.
Rhages. 13th century.   D. 11·9 in.

Fig. 50. Bowl of similar ware painted in blue, brownish red, black, and white enamels with touches of leaf gilding. Subject, a throned figure and attendants and four winged animals with human heads: border of ornamental Cufic characters. Outside is a Naskhi inscription.
Rhages. 13th century.   D. 8·4 in.

Burāq, the winged steed which carried Mohammed to Paradise, is represented as human-headed. These sphinx-like animals which figure so frequently on painted Rhages pottery probably represent 'steeds of paradise'.

Fig. 51. Bowl of similar ware painted in blue, turquoise, manganese, red, and black enamels.
Rhages. 13th century.   D. 8·3 in.

Fig. 52. Bowl of similar ware delicately painted in green, red, blue, yellow, and brown on a pale turquoise blue glaze. The Cufic characters on the inner border have been read as a repetition of *alvafi* (the Faithful One). Outside is a Naskhi inscription which has been rendered: 'May your occupation be ever full of joy, pleasure, and cheerfulness—Your companions ever be prosperity, victory, and happiness. Do not doubt of my sorrow at your happiness, and of my having rent the garment of patience. . . .'
Said to have been found at Veramin.
Rhages ware. 13th century.   D. 8·25 in.

FIG. 53. Bowl with cheetah handles and two spouts in the form of deer heads. Similar ware painted in blue, turquoise green, red, and black enamels.
Rhages. 13th century.   H. 6·5 in.

FIG. 54. Bowl of similar ware with ornament partly built up in relief and partly enamelled in blue, turquoise, green, red, and black: the embossed portions white and gilt. Inside are painted *sīmurghs* among embossed arabesques. Outside are six throned figures with embossed arabesques between. There is blue glaze on the base.
From Khar. 13th century.   D. 9·25 in.
See coloured postcard C 202.

FIG. 55. Dish of sandy white ware with deep blue glaze, on which are designs in red and white enamels and leaf gilding. Radial lines in white on the exterior.
Rhages. 13th century.   D. 13·9 in.
See coloured postcard C 200.

FIG. 56. Bowl of similar ware.
Rhages. 13th century.   D. 6·5 in.

FIG. 57. Shallow basin of sandy white ware with boldly carved foliage scroll under a deep blue glaze.
Rhages or Sulṭānābād. 13th century.   D. 10·8 in.
See coloured postcard C 206.

FIG. 58. Bowl of sandy white ware coated outside with black slip through which are incised a band of Naskhi inscription and a band of radial lines: the whole is covered with a pale turquoise blue glaze.
Rhages. 13th century.   D. 6·75 in.
See coloured postcard C 207.

FIG. 59. Bowl of sandy white ware painted in blue and brown-black under a clear glaze. On the brown bands inside are incised inscriptions, an illegible mixture of Arabic and Persian.
Rhages. 13th century. (Van den Bergh Collection.)   D. 8·9 in.

FIG. 60. Part of a bowl of sandy white pottery with carved knot pattern, pierced and filled with clear glaze.
Found at Rhages.   L. 0·75 in.

FIG. 61. Bowl of similar ware with pierced cable border filled with glaze and painted design of a hare in blue and brown.
Probably Rhages. 13th century.   D. 5·2 in.

FIG. 62. Part of a bowl of sandy buff white ware with carved designs pierced and filled with blue glaze.
From Fosṭāṭ.   L. 2·8 in.

FIG. 63. Dish of reddish buff pottery with dressing of white slip painted in brown-black and light blue under a clear glaze. The reverse is unglazed.
Veramin (?). 14th century.   D. 11·4 in.

FIG. 64. Bowl of red pottery with dressing of white slip painted inside in dark blue and manganese purple with radiating plant designs

and formal characters under a transparent crackled glaze. Small
base with rim broken away.
Probably 14th century.   D. 7·4 in.
The ware is similar to that found at Miletus.

FIG. 65. Bottle of sandy white ware with ornament moulded in relief
under a green glaze. On the body is a band of Cufic characters
(viz. *baraka* and other words meaning 'blessings') among floral
scrolls.
13th century.   H. 9 in.

FIG. 66. Bottle of similar ware with pale blue glaze. Seed pattern
on the shoulders.
13th century.   H. 9·55 in.

FIG. 67. Ewer of metal form. Sandy white ware with ornament (inscriptions and scrolls) in relief under a pale turquoise blue glaze.
13th century.   H. 8·9 in.

FIG. 68. Bowl of soft, sandy ware, greyish white in colour: decorated
in blue and brown and in white slip under a clear glaze. Inside is
a medallion with a camel among flowers and foliage reserved in
greyish white, with outlines and details in brown, in a blue ground.
On the sides are five seated figures of Mongol type in a ground of
lotuses and other flowers, and foliage: the designs slightly raised in
white slip and outlined and shaded with brown: the grey background is hatched with brown. Outside is a band of formal Naskhi
inscription in white relief against a blue ground; and elsewhere
there are floral scrolls in blue and brown.
'Sulṭānābād.' Late 13th century.   D. 16·2 in.

FIG. 69. Bowl with curved sides and small deep base. Sandy greyish
ware painted in dark blue, turquoise, and black under a clear glaze.
In alternate compartments are cranes in turquoise foliage, the
background hatched with black; and between them is raised white
foliage in a blue ground.
'Sulṭānābād.' 13th century. (Van den Bergh Collection).
                                                          D. 8·5 in.

FIG. 70. Dish of sandy whitish pottery painted in blue and brown
under a clear glaze. The peacock in the central medallion is outlined and shaded in brown, and the surrounding foliage, similarly
outlined, is set in a blue ground.
13th century.   D. 12·7 in.

FIG. 71. Dish of sandy whitish pottery painted in blue and brown
under a clear glaze. Said to have been excavated near Teheran.
                                                          D. 8·9 in.

FIG. 72. Part of the bottom of a bowl of sandy white ware painted
with geometrical designs in blue, brown-black, and turquoise under
a clear glaze. The remains of a kiln-support and a piece of another
vessel adhering show that this is a 'waster'.
14th century (?).   D. 3·75 in.
From the site of a pottery at Damascus.

PLATE XXIII

FIG. 78. LUSTRED BOTTLE: SEVENTEENTH CENTURY

FIG. 73. Shallow bowl of sandy whitish pottery painted in blue and brown and a little turquoise under a clear glaze.
Syrian (?). 13th or 14th century. D. 8 in.

FIG. 74. Lower part of an *albarello* with sides moulded in tiers of arched compartments. Reddish buff pottery with thick blue glaze on which are painted in lustre inscriptions alternating with scrolls. From Fosṭāṭ. 14th century. H. 6·8 in.

FIG. 75. Bowl with gently rounded sides and small base. Sandy white pottery painted in blue and black under a clear glaze. There are radial lines on the exterior; and a mark consisting of two indeterminate strokes on the base.
Probably Egyptian. 14th century. D. 9·6 in.

FIG. 76. Vase of buff pottery with dressing of white slip decorated in blue and brown under a clear glaze. Said to have come from Fosṭāṭ. 14th century. H. 14·7 in.
See coloured postcard C 209.

FIG. 77. Dish of sandy buff white pottery with dotted designs—two fishes and groups of dots suggesting flowers—under a pea-green 'celadon' glaze which breaks into accidental splashes of dark crimson on the fluted sides.
Probably Egyptian. 15th Century. (Van den Bergh Collection.)
D. 9·6 in.

PERIOD III

LATE PERSIAN POTTERY

IN the third period admirable pottery was still made during the sixteenth and seventeenth centuries but, though the technique remained much the same, the whole character of the ware was altered by changes in the style of the decoration.

The Persian style was now profoundly affected by two influences. One came from Anatolia, where a brilliant school of ceramists was established under the Turks; and the other from China. Chinese influences were nothing new in Persia, but now they become predominant; and whole groups of Persian pottery are so completely penetrated by them that one would say the potters' aim was to pass their goods off as Chinese.

Practically the only type of ware not deeply affected by these two influences is the lustre ware which is reputed to be of the Shah Abbas period; and this could hardly be otherwise, as neither Anatolia nor China used the lustre pigment. A series of this lustred pottery can be seen in Case B of Bay XXVII where it stands in striking contrast with the earlier lustre wares in the adjoining Case. The background is no longer the opaque creamy white glaze of Rhages; and the lustre is painted on the clear silicious glaze which covers the pure white and often translucent body so characteristic of Persian pottery at this time. This body is apparently only a modification of the early, sandy white ware, but it is finer in grain, closer in texture, and so deeply penetrated by the glass of the glaze that it is actually translucent. It has in fact many of the qualities of porcelain without its hardness, for it will still powder easily under the knife.

The glaze of this lustred ware is either left white, or tinted with blue, dark or light, or more rarely with yellow. One specimen is

Fig. 79. Lustred bottle with European mount. 17th century.

olive brown with an over-all lustre, but as a rule the lustre is painted in free, sketchy designs, mostly trees and plants among which are shapes resembling the cypress though not drawn to scale: animals such as the zebu, hare, &c., and occasionally birds: and formal patterns—arabesque scrolls, leaf-shaped medallions, &c.— and cable borders. Spur-marks are prominent on the bases. The lustre is greenish brown, or reddish brown in colour, and its reflections are generally coppery, sometimes ruby. The early practice of reserving the design in a lustre ground seems to have been abandoned.

With regard to the dating of this group the only document we

PLATE XXIV

FIG. 80. LUSTRED BOWL: SEVENTEENTH CENTURY

PLATE XXV

Fig. 81. EWER DATED 1616

have is a bottle described by H. Wallis,[1] which bears a date variously read A.H. 1062 and 1084 (=A.D. 1651 or 1673). Another bottle, in the Collection, has a European metal mount of about the year 1700 (fig. 79). This seventeenth-century date is confirmed by the shapes of the dishes, ewers, vases, and bowls.

Chardin, who travelled extensively in Persia in the seventeenth century, wrote of the pottery as one of the most beautiful products of the country and as being made in all parts. The best, he says, came from Shiraz, Meshed, Yezd, Kirmān, and Zarand in Kirmania. The material was as pure as that of Chinese porcelain, of as

FIG. 82. Persian bowl. 17th century.

fine grain, and as transparent. In fact, people were often deceived into thinking that it was really Chinese. Elsewhere he goes further, stating that the Dutch traders actually sent Persian pottery to Europe and passed it off as Chinese: and it may be added that it is no uncommon thing even to this day to find Persian blue and white mixed with Chinese porcelain and mistaken for it.

Chardin speaks chiefly of the material, but it is in the decoration far more than in the material that we notice the conscious effort to copy the Chinese. This is particularly noticeable in the blue-painted wares which closely follow the late Ming blue and white. There are numerous specimens of this in Case A of Bay XXVII, notably the interesting kettle-shaped ewer (fig. 81) which bears the inscriptions 'The decorator of it the poor Zarī, 1025' (=A.D. 1616) and 'The work of Maḥmūd Mi'mār of Yezd'. The designs—panels of landscape with flowering plants, geese, and a deer—and

---

[1] *Typical Examples of Persian Ceramic Art*, Pl. II.

the borders of *ju-i* heads and 'false gadroons' are pure Chinese and should be compared with the export Ming porcelain in Bay XXXII, both for the style of decoration and the quality of the blue. It is not often that we can assign a specimen of old Persian pottery to a definite locality; but here we have an authenticated example of

Fig. 84. Dish, dated 1697/8.

the ware of Yezd. It does not, however, help us greatly in the identification of other specimens, for its characteristics are common to all the high-class Persian wares of the period. The body is the fine, but rather loose-grained, white material with a clear glaze, the kind which is translucent in its thinner parts and in some ways comparable with the artificial porcelains of Europe. Another specimen found at Yezd, and probably of Yezd make, is the saucer dish in the same Case with a large cactus-like design filled in with formal foliage and blossoms. There is, however, nothing Chinese about this design, though the reverse of the dish has four Chinese symbols.

PLATE XXVI

Fig. 83. PERSIAN BOTTLE: SEVENTEENTH CENTURY

The blue of the Persian blue-and-white is often of fine quality, and even on the common specimens it is in no way inferior to the Chinese. It is slightly purplish in tone, resembling in this quality the Mohammedan blue of the Ming period; and like the latter it is soft and inclined to be hazy and to run in the outlines.

Fig. 85. Persian dish, about 1700.

Though Chinese influences dominate this class of Persian ware, the details of the designs are not slavishly copied, and the flowers are often obviously of Persian growth though rendered in the Chinese style. Thus the favouritè floral scroll used for filling and for borders, &c., though derived from the Chinese lily scroll, has a leaf sometimes like ivy and sometimes like oak (fig. 85) which is not found on Chinese wares. Moreover, in many cases the blue and white designs are outlined and even shaded with brown-black, a Near-Eastern technique which is quite un-Chinese; but even in these cases we find imitations of Chinese marks on the bottoms of dishes and bowls, showing that Chinese ideas were ever present in the potters' minds.

In the blue and white group the objects which show specific Chinese influences are a large bowl (fig. 82) at the West end of Table-case H which has flying cranes and clouds, pheasants and flowering plants on the sides, and a mark in which Chinese characters are roughly suggested: and others in Case A of Bay XXVII such as the dish with an archaic dragon in a star-shaped panel, the two

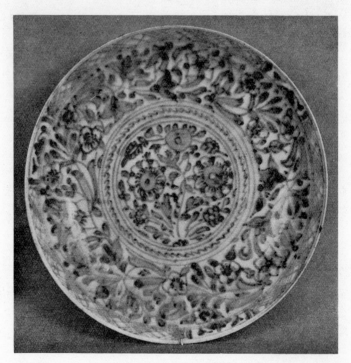

FIG. 86. Dish, dated 1817.

sprinklers with Chinese figures in landscape in late Ming style, and the hookah-base with mammiform spout painted in late Ming style.

In the rest the Chinese influence is only of a general kind and disguised by designs in Persian taste. One small series represented by a dish and an elegant bottle (fig. 83) is notable for the treatment of foliage, which is white shaded with black and reserved in a blue ground. The dish has a mock Chinese mark.

Interesting for dated inscriptions are (1) the large dish (fig. 84) with lotus plants and pagodas adapted from the Chinese and an inscribed border which includes the passage 'finished in the year

1109'[1] (=A.D. 1697/8); and (2) a dish with floral scrolls (fig. 86), and legend on the base 'Belonging to Aḥmad, made by Muḥammad 'Alī 1232' (=A.D. 1817).

In addition to the blue and white, numerous other types of Chinese porcelain were copied by the Persian potters. Thus an

FIG. 87. Persian ewer. 17th century.

elegant ewer (fig. 87) at the East end of Table-case H is decorated with designs in raised outlines and filled with white and yellow glazes in a ground of aubergine purple, in the style of Ming three-colour ware of the *cloisonné* type.[2] Another Ming ware is imitated by the large dish (fig. 88) and a vase in Case F of Bay XXVIII with white slip designs on a celadon green glaze. In both instances the designs are Persian in feeling though the technique is Chinese.

[1] The numerals are not perfectly clear, and the date might be read 1009 or 1109, i.e. A.D. 1600/1 or 1697/8.

[2] See *Guide to the Pottery and Porcelain of the Far East*, p. 42.

White slip decoration was used in China on other glazes besides the celadon, on blue and brown for instance ; and of these the Persian potters certainly adopted the blue, for fragments of both blue and celadon Persian wares with slip designs were found at Bijapur in India, a city destroyed about 1680.

Painted decoration in blue and red under the glaze was used on Chinese porcelain in Ming times and to a larger extent in the early

FIG. 88. Persian 'celadon' dish. 17th century.

decades of the eighteenth century. Two bottles and two bowls in Case A of Bay XXVII illustrate the Near-Eastern version of this combination, but it will be noticed that, instead of the vivid red derived from copper oxide which is a feature of the Chinese ware, the Persian potter has been perforce content with a dull maroon colour in the form of an earthy slip which, like the Turkish red, stands up in palpable relief (fig. 89).

The Chinese *famille rose* enamels found their way to Persia in due course, but they came when the eighteenth century was well advanced and at a time when Persian ceramic art was in its decline. They are represented by the rose pink and other enamels on a jar with modern metal mounts in Case A of Bay XXVII.

The imitation of Chinese monochromes has already been noted among the wares of an earlier period (p. 60). It continued to be freely practised by the later Persian potters, and there are numerous examples in the Collection, chiefly in Case F of Bay XXVIII, where one can see glazes copying the deep blue, lavender blue,

FIG. 89. Narghili, about 1700.

lavender grey or *clair de lune*, turquoise, celadon green, and coffee brown. A dainty saucer placed with the 'Gombroon' types in Case B of Bay XXVII has a celadon glaze outside, while the interior is white with incised floral designs in Chinese style.

A bowl with coffee brown glaze in the middle of Case F of Bay XXVIII has been decorated on the lapidary's wheel with floral designs cut through the brown covering into the white body; but this embellishment was doubtless added in Europe.

A somewhat similar effect produced by pure ceramic means is seen on a sherbet bowl in the upper section of the same Case. This piece is covered with a brown slip through which the ornament is scratched deep enough to reveal the white body beneath. The glaze is transparent and colourless. Here we have a survival of the old Persian technique of *graffiato* designs in black or brown slip, which was noted in connexion with Rhages pottery (p. 50), but the designs themselves in the present instance are in Chinese taste.

'GOMBROON' WARE

Mention has been made (p. 17) of the pleasing effect of the pierced decoration of some early Persian wares in which the inter-

FIG. 90. Bowl of 'Gombroon' ware. 18th century.

stices are filled with clear glaze forming transparencies. This technique was employed with happy results on the translucent lettuce-white pottery of the third period. There are several good examples, in the form of bowls (fig. 90) and dishes, in Case A of Bay XXVII. Most of them have slight supplementary ornament painted in black, which only serves to enhance the lightness and beauty of the white material.

It is not certain where this ware was made, or indeed if its manufacture was limited to one or two centres. The name Gombroon, with which tradition has labelled it, cannot refer to anything more than the place of export. Gombroon, opposite

Ormuz, in the Persian Gulf, is a port in which the English East
India Company had an establishment from about 1600 onward. It
was an entrepôt for the Far-Eastern trade, and goods shipped from
Gombroon included Chinese porcelain as well as Persian pottery.
So we do not know whether Walpole's 'two basins of the most
ancient Gombroon china', to quote the Catalogue of the Straw-
berry Hill Collection, were of Far- or Near-Eastern make: but
it is evident that Martin Lister writing in 1698 implied a Persian
manufacture when he compared St. Cloud porcelain with the
'Gombroon ware which is, indeed, little else but a total vitrification'. For he goes on to contrast it with Chinese porcelain.

It is possible, though by no means certain, that Lister is here
alluding to the type of Persian pottery now under consideration,
for its translucency might well suggest 'total vitrification'; and
in that case we should have evidence of the existence of the ware
at the end of the seventeenth century. But indeed we may regard
this date as already proved, for among the fragments from the
site of Bijapur in India, a city destroyed about 1680, are pieces
of this kind of Persian ware.

There are a few dated specimens in this and other collections, but
they belong to the eighteenth and the early part of the nineteenth
century, e.g. a bowl in Case A of Bay XXVII inscribed 'made by
Muḥammad 'Alī A.H. 1234' (=A.D. 1819). We may, then, regard
the so-called Gombroon ware as ranging from the seventeenth
century onwards. The technique is one which, as already stated,
the Chinese borrowed from Persia, for the so-called 'rice-grain'
porcelain of China[1] does not appear to go back farther than the
reign of Ch'ien Lung (1736–95).

KUBATCHA

Daghestan in the region of the Caucasus and the Caspian is
alleged to be the home of certain kinds of ware which belong to
our third period; and the village of Kubatcha in particular has
been made to sponsor a rather crude but decorative pottery
painted in blue, green, yellow, and a pale red slip which remotely
resembles the red of the Turkish wares, under a clear glaze which
is often widely crazed or crackled. The ware itself is a coarse, sandy
material, the buff tone of which is concealed by a wash of white
slip. Female heads surrounded with flowers, or floral designs, and
animals in Chinese style, form the usual decoration, and this class
of ware seems to belong to the sixteenth and seventeenth centuries,[2]

[1] See *Guide to the Pottery and Porcelain of the Far East*, p. 95. The rice-
grain porcelain has transparencies formed by excisions of about the shape
and size of a grain of rice, which are filled by clear glaze: hence the name.
[2] Two tablets in the Victoria and Albert Museum, dated in 1593, belong
to this type of ware.

though it is frequently given an earlier date. As to its provenance, all the information we have is a dealer's report that dishes of this kind have been found at Kubatcha, but there is no serious evidence that it was made in this district. Specimens can be seen in the Loan Court of the Victoria and Albert Museum in the Kelekian Collection. The Catalogue of the same Collection includes

Fig. 91. Dish, Persian or Syrian. 16th century.

a dish[1] of another type which is also attributed to Daghestan on equally slender evidence. It is decorated in black under a turquoise blue glaze and belongs to a class of which there are several examples in the lower part of Case B of Bay XXVII and in the West end of Table-case H. The interest in this particular specimen is that it has an inscription with date A.H. 873=A.D. 1469. Other examples of this kind of ware have a green glaze instead of the turquoise blue. The glaze is often crazed, and consequently it has become stained and clouded in use. We regard them as belonging to the fifteenth and sixteenth centuries (fig. 91). There

[1] *Catalogue of the Kelekian Collection of Persian and Analogous Potteries,* Plate LXXXI.

is nothing new in the technique of these wares. Black designs under turquoise glaze belong to both our earlier periods. But the style of decoration in this group is different from that of the earlier specimens and shows in many cases the influence of the Anatolian style of Turkish pottery.

It is improbable that this simple type belongs to any particular district. It is found in various parts of the Near East. One vase in the Collection with designs of rather a Chinese flavour is reputed to have come from Bokhara, and two dishes with ornament closely resembling that of the Turkish wares of Anatolia came from the village of Arba'īn, on the northern outskirts of Damascus.

Marks are occasionally seen on the late Persian wares. They consist of signatures, such as the name Ḥātim which is inscribed inside the bowl of fig. 80, and in the inscription on the base of fig. 81 : imitations of Chinese characters or seal-marks, particularly on the 'blue and white' types; and a few indefinite signs, such as a V-shaped mark crossed by two strokes, and a sign which might be named the 'tassel' mark (Plate XXXIX). This last consists of a row of four or five loops (perhaps intended to suggest writing), below which is an inverted pyramid of horizontal strokes finished off, in the more carefully drawn examples, with a tassel. Varieties of this mark appear on figs. 84, 85, and 89. The hare painted in lustre on the bottom of the seventeenth-century lustre bowl in Case B of Bay XXVII may be merely a *jeu d'esprit* of the decorator, or it may have been inspired by the 'hare mark' which occurs occasionally on Chinese blue and white porcelain of the late Ming period.

FIG. 78. Bottle, pear-shaped, of sandy, white semi-porcelain painted in lustre on a violet blue glaze.
17th century.   H. 9 in.
See coloured postcard C 210.

FIG. 79. Bottle of similar ware painted in lustre on a clear glaze on the body and on a blue glaze on the neck and shoulder. A European metal mount and cover have converted it into a jug.
17th century.   H. 5·8 in.

FIG. 80. Covered bowl with spout. Similar ware painted in lustre on a violet blue glaze outside and on a clear glaze inside. Inside is the signature *Ḥātim*.
17th century.   H. 5·7 in.

FIG. 81. Ewer of sandy, white semi-porcelain painted in blue under a clear glaze with panel designs and border patterns in the style of Chinese late Ming blue and white porcelain. Inscribed in Naskhi characters 'The work of Maḥmūd Mi'mār of Yezd' and 'The decorator of it the poor Zarī 1025' (= A.D. 1616).   H. 9·8 in.

FIG. 82. Bowl of similar ware painted in blue with black outlines under a clear glaze. Inside is a medallion with a wolf (?) in a ground of floral scrolls, with flying cranes and clouds in Chinese style on the

sides. Outside are pheasants and flowering plants in Chinese style.
Square mark on the base imitating Chinese.   D. 15·4 in.

FIG. 83. Bottle, flask-shaped, of sandy, white semi-porcelain painted
in black and pale blue under a clear glaze. Round the sunk medallion in the centre are flowers with characteristically shaded foliage,
set in a blue ground.   H. 11·5 in.

FIG. 84. Dish of similar ware painted in blue and brown under a clear
glaze. Designs in Chinese style in the centre, and black panels on
the sides with etched inscriptions, mostly poetry, but including the
sentence 'finished in the year 1109' (= A.D. 1697/8). 'Oak-leaf'
scrolls on the rim. Tassel mark on the base (Plate XXXIX).
                                                         D. 17·2 in.
The second figure of the date is not quite clear. It could alter-
natively be read A.H. 1009 (= A.D. 1600/1).

FIG. 85. Dish of similar ware painted in blue under a clear glaze.
Lotus and 'oak-leaf' scroll border. Tassel mark on the base
(Plate XXXIX).   D. 18·3 in.

FIG. 86. Dish of sandy, white semi-porcelain, painted in blue under
a clear glaze. Mark on the base 'Belonging to Aḥmad, made by
Muḥammad 'Alī A.H. 1232' (= A.D. 1817).   D. 8·25 in.

FIG. 87. Ewer of sandy white ware with turquoise blue glaze and
panels with floral scrolls outlined in relief and filled with white and
yellow glazes in a ground of aubergine purple. Metal spout, handle,
cover, and lining.
17th century.   H. 14 in.

FIG. 88. Dish of sandy white ware with 'celadon' green glaze and
ornament painted in white slip.
About 1700.   D. 15·3 in.

FIG. 89. Narghili of similar ware painted in blue, black, and liver red
slips under a clear glaze. Two mounted huntsmen, one with a
falcon and an attendant, finding a lady bathing in a stream, are
depicted among flowers and foliage on the body. The scene no
doubt represents Khusrau finding Shīrīn. Tassel mark on the base.
About 1700.   H. 11·7 in.

FIG. 90. Bowl of sandy, white semi-porcelain with border of transparencies and ornament in black.
18th century.   D. 4·8 in.

FIG. 91. Dish of sandy buff ware painted in black under a turquoise
blue glaze.
Persian or Syrian. 16th century.   D. 13·4 in.

TURKISH POTTERY

Glazed pottery was used in the form of mosaic tiles and bricks
in the mosques and public buildings of Asia Minor during the
thirteenth, fourteenth, and fifteenth centuries.[1] The earliest

[1] See Migeon and Sakisian, *La Céramique d'Asie-Mineure et de Constantinople*, Paris, 1923, pp. 5–16.

published examples are wall decorations on the buildings at Konia, among which is the Sirtchali Médressé, built in 1243. Fourteenth-century examples are found at Nicaea; and the famous green mosque and green tower at Brusa, the capital of the Ottoman Turks, were built in 1419 and 1421. Here the coloured glazes included dark blue, turquoise, white and black, yellow and green; and the decorative motives, inscriptions, geometrical designs, scrolls, conventional Chinese lotus, and the naturalistic flowers of the Herat school. Gilding was sometimes used. There is also fifteenth-century mosaic tilework in Constantinople.

In several instances the names of Persian artists are found inscribed on these wall tiles, and it may be assumed that the art of mosaic tilework was brought from Persia and first practised in Asia Minor by Persian workmen. The supposition is confirmed by the general style of the work, which has a pronounced Persian flavour. A further influx of Persian workmen took place in 1514 when the Sultan Selīm I captured Tabriz and took seven hundred families of artificers to Constantinople.

Little is known of the ordinary pottery made in Asia Minor before the sixteenth century. A few blue and white bowls were found in the excavations at Ephesus.[1]

FIG. 92. *Albarello*, with blue decoration. 15th century.

They are painted with floral scrolls in Perso-Chinese taste like those of fig. 92; and as similar designs appear on fifteenth-century tiles[2] from a mosque at Damascus, we may regard these bowls as a type common to Syria, Persia, and Asia Minor in the fifteenth century. French writers[3] assign certain blue and white lamps, similar to fig. 93, to this century. Their stylized lotus scrolls

---

[1] See p. 30. Similar ware, found in excavations at Miletus, is in the Kaiser Friedrich Museum, Berlin.

[2] Exhibited in the Victoria and Albert Museum.

[3] Migeon and Sakisian, p. 29 and figs. 13 and 14.

certainly have affinities with the Perso-Chinese blue and white
of the time; and it is further agreed that the Cufic inscriptions
which they bear belong in style to this century rather than to
the sixteenth. Arabesque foliage reserved in white in a deep blue
ground is another feature of these lamps and connects them with
other specimens (fig. 94) which will be discussed presently.

FIG. 93. Turkish pottery lamp. About 1500.

There is, for instance, a series of lamps, jugs, ewers, bowls, &c., in
the Godman Collection[1] decorated in two shades of blue in this
style, which is grouped under the heading of Kutāhiya; and this
nomenclature has been widely accepted. It is, however, based
entirely on a blue and white ewer in this group,[2] decorated chiefly
with flowers and arabesque foliage in white reserved in a blue
ground, and which has in addition an inscription in Armenian
writing. The reading of this inscription is given in the intro-
duction to the Catalogue, 'This mass cruet commemorates the
servant of God, Abraham of Kutāhiya, anno armen. 959' (=A.D.
1510). The date is important as proving that ware of this kind was

---

[1] *Catalogue of the Godman Collection of Oriental and Spanish Pottery and
Glass*, 1901, p. 52.   [2] *Ibid.*, p. 52, No. 7.

PLATE XXVII

FIG. 94. TURKISH POTTERY BOWL ABOUT 1500

made in the early years of the sixteenth century; and it shows that the French attribution of certain members of the group to the preceding century is perfectly reasonable. For the rest it is impossible to agree that this inscription fixes the manufacture of this ware in Kutāhiya. All we may legitimately infer is that the ewer in question was made for a dignitary of that place, and as there is apparently no tradition of pottery made at Kutāhiya before the seventeenth century, we must find some other centre of manufacture for this ware.

The most likely place is Isnik (Nicaea), a town situated about forty miles north-east of Brusa and about the same distance from the Sea of Marmora. Though no record exists of the origin of the potteries in this place, it is proved beyond doubt that it was an important centre of ceramic activity in the sixteenth century. We shall return to this point presently, but for the moment it is enough to note one relevant fact, namely that among the tiles in the Isnik mosque, examined by Dr. Martin,[1] were many decorated in two shades of blue in the style of the so-called Kutāhiya ware.

The Turkish pottery so far discussed has been characterized by the Persian or Syrian types of design, which were in themselves much influenced by Chinese porcelain. It specialized in arabesque foliage and scrolls of highly conventionalized flowers. Towards the middle of the sixteenth century there developed in the Turkish dominions a new and striking style of pottery decoration in which bold designs of naturalistic flowers are the outstanding feature. There are three classes of this Turkish ware, showing small differences in style but wide differences in colour.

The first and most characteristic group is distinguished by the use of a brilliant tomato red, which is usually combined with blue, leaf green, turquoise, and black, the last used for outlining the designs.

In this group the rendering of flowers is very naturalistic and one recognizes the rose, carnation, tulip, hyacinth, fritillary, &c., in the elegant sprays thrown artistically across the fine white surface of the ware, or, in some cases, reserved in a single-coloured ground of red, green, lavender, or coffee brown. But besides the natural shapes there are, even in this group, conventional renderings of plant motives, such as the cypress tree drawn out of scale, long feathery palm-like leaves, and palmettes jewelled with imaginary blossoms. These conventionalized designs form the connecting link between this group and the second, which has long passed under the name of Damascus ware.

In this second group a pale aubergine purple derived from manganese replaces the upstanding tomato red, and the prevailing

[1] See *Burlington Magazine*, Aug. 1909, 'The True Origin of So-called Damascus Ware', by Dr. F. R. Martin.

green colour has a sage or verdigris tint (fig. 101). Several shades of blue are used, but the brilliant dark blue and the black outlines are similar to those of Group I. As for the designs, they are equally floral, but the flowers are more conventionalized, and much use is made of the long, feathery leaf and the flowered palmettes.

Group III is a variant of this group, in which similar designs are rendered in two shades of blue, the technique being very like that of the earlier blue and white which we have just discussed in connexion with Kutāhiya and Isnik.

It should be added that in all three groups the ware is essentially the same, a fine-grained but rather sandy material soft enough to powder under the knife and similar to, though rather finer in texture than, the standard bodies of Syria and Persia. The colour of this ware is an impure white, but this impurity is masked on the exposed surfaces by a dressing of fine white slip. On this surface the designs are painted in blue, or outlined in black and filled in with the various colours; and the whole is covered with a clear, transparent silicious glaze.

Ceramic nomenclature has been too often hasty and ill considered. The need for distinctive names for the different types of ware was urgent, and usually the first plausible suggestion has been accepted by an uncritical public and straightway consecrated by usage.

Attention was first drawn to the ware by specimens with the tomato red colour (Group I) which had been found at Lindos in Rhodes; and it was at once assumed that Rhodes was the birthplace of this beautiful pottery, which decorates half the Turkish buildings in Asia Minor. Nothing could have been more improbable; but the name Rhodian became current for this ware, and although the fallacy has been exposed so often that the arguments are not worth repeating, 'Rhodian', like 'Old Nanking' and 'Oriental Lowestoft', though banished from self-respecting Museums and scientific books, is a term still freely used in the sale-room and the shop.

Similarly the term 'Damascus ware' for Groups II and III remained unchallenged until 1909, when Dr. F. Martin raised the question of the 'true origin of the so-called Damascus ware' in an article in the *Burlington Magazine*.[1] There was more reason for the nomenclature in this case, for many of the buildings at Damascus are adorned with tiles of various kinds, and among them are some with designs in blue, manganese, and sage green which belong to our second group: but this is hardly sufficient ground for crediting Damascus with the whole output of this particular ware and its allied types. There were certainly potteries at Damascus, and the industry probably flourished there in pre-Turkish days (see p. 57); but when Syria was conquered by the Turks in 1517, it is

[1] *Loc. cit.*

stated that the best craftsmen were removed from Damascus to Constantinople, just as they had been from Tabriz three years before.

Of all the Turkish pottery there is nothing finer than the members of Group II at their best; and their best belong to the period about 1549, the date of the mosque lamp (Frontispiece) in Case E of Bay XXVII. It would seem logical to look for the source of this splendid ware not in the depleted potteries of Damascus but in some centre where the Turks had concentrated the talent which their conquests had gathered in. Moreover, in the public baths at Brusa, which were restored in the sixteenth century by Rustem Pasha, Dr. Martin saw thousands of tiles of the finest quality which belong to our second group, and this would give Brusa at least an equal claim with Damascus to the honour of originating the ware. But Brusa had ceased to be the capital of the Turks for the best part of a century; and one would look nearer to the new capital, Constantinople, for the centre of Turkish ceramic activity in the sixteenth century.

Again there is evidence pointing in the direction of Isnik (Nicaea). It is supplied by Migeon and Sakisian,[1] who quote Gerlach's reference in 1577 to an order for tiles from Nicaea and to his further statement that 'they also make dishes, drinking vessels, and other domestic utensils in the potteries of this place'. The same authors quote an order from the Sultan Murād III in 1589 to the magistrate of Nicaea bidding him expedite the delivery of tiles for a new pavilion in Constantinople. Further, the late sixteenth century Turkish chronicler, Saadeddin, adds his testimony that 'the clay of Nicaea produces faïence vessels such as words fail to describe. It is hard to distinguish them from Chinese porcelain, and the faïence used in the mosques and the great buildings which are put up in Turkey is made in this town.'

It is probable that there were potteries at Constantinople and in many other places in the Turkish dominions, but evidently those of Isnik were the most important in the sixteenth century. The early history of the industry there is obscure. Local tradition ascribes its origin variously to Chinese and Persian potters in the first years of the fifteenth century; but Nicaea was a place of much importance long before the Turkish conquest, and it is probable that its potteries go back to much more ancient times.[2] It suffered a heavy decline in the seventeenth century; for Evlia Tchélébi[3] writing in 1698 says 'there are workshops of master

[1] *La Céramique d'Asie-Mineure et de Constantinople*, Paris, 1923, pp. 26 and 27.

[2] See A. J. Butler, *Islamic Pottery*, p. 166. The same writer (*ibid.*, p. 165) alludes to the manufacture of tiles at the neighbouring city of Nicomedia (Ismid) in the twelfth century. The evidence for this is in the use of the two words τάνοτρια Νικομήδεια in Byzantine Greek records, the former of them being taken to mean 'tiles'.

[3] Quoted by Migeon and Sakisian, *op. cit.*, p. 39.

potters in nine districts of this town. In the time of Aḥmad Khān
(1603–1607) there were three hundred. They have been ruined
by persecutions'. But there is evidence (p. 91) that the industry
was still lingering on at Isnik in the eighteenth century.

We have already suggested that the finely decorated blue and
white pottery such as figs. 93 and 94, which was formerly assigned
to Kutāhiya, should be transferred to Isnik. It remains to find
evidence that the other three groups discussed on p. 82 have the

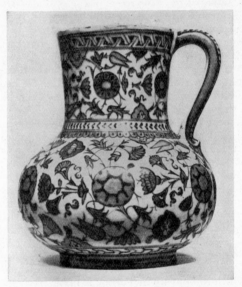

FIG. 95. Turkish jug. 16th century.

same origin. As far as Group I is concerned, that with the naturalistic flowers and the peculiar tomato-red pigment, no one disputes
any longer that it was chiefly made at Isnik, and that the correct
description of it is Turkish and not Rhodian.

With regard to Group II we have Dr. Martin's statement[1] that
more fragments of the so-called Damascus plates are to be found
at Isnik than anywhere else; and apart from this important
evidence, based on personal observation, there is internal evidence
in the decoration of various specimens which seems to bring all
the Turkish types so far described into close relationship. We have
already noted that the material of the ware is virtually the same in
all cases. In Pier-case F of Bay XXVII is a series of jugs, some decorated in the two blues of our third group (fig. 95), and others with
the same blues reinforced with the manganese purple and sage

[1] *Burlington Magazine, loc. cit.*

green of the so-called Damascus type (fig. 96). These and other specimens show conclusively that Groups II and III belong to the same family. Another jug (fig. 97) in Pier-case D of the same Bay has all the characteristics of this series, but with a thin Turkish red instead of manganese. Here, then, is one link between Groups I and II. Another is to be seen in the three dishes (fig. 98) in the lower part of the adjoining Pier-case E, which have the large feathery leaves and the much conventionalized flowers of Group II but

FIGS. 96 and 97. Turkish jugs. 16th century.

also the Turkish red and the border design of 'ammonite scrolls' which is a commonplace on the Turkish dishes of Group I.

The relationship between Group III, that painted in two blues, and Group I, that with the Turkish red, is definitely established by a dish on the top shelf of Pier-case F (fig. 99), which is painted in the two blues but with a design of naturalistic flowers which have all the characteristics of Group I even to the broken stem of one of the sprays (see p. 88).

These are only a few cases, but a glance at Cases D, E, F of Bay XXVII will serve to show the family likeness in all three groups. To complete the connexion it would be interesting to link up Group II with the so-called 'Kutāhiya' types illustrated by figs.

93 and 94.   This can be done with the aid of certain tiles in the
Musée des Arts Décoratifs in Paris. They are illustrated in *L'Art
de l'Islam* by R. Koechlin (Plates 34 and 35, figs. 135 and 136);
and they show floral designs in the so-called 'Damascus' colouring,
surrounding vases which are decorated in white reserved in blue
with precisely the same arabesque foliage that covers the exterior
of our fig. 94. Again Plate 35, fig. 137, of the same publication,

FIG. 98. Turkish pottery dish. 16th century.

shows a similar tile with a vase decorated with Turkish sailing
boats, a design much more appropriate to the wares of Nicaea, a
city on a lake near the Sea of Marmora, than to those of Damascus.

From these considerations it is clear that 'Damascus ware' as
a generic term for our second group should be abandoned, and
that it would be safer to give the general name of Turkish to all
three groups. All of them were probably made at Isnik, though
there is no reason to suppose that Isnik was the only locality in
which pottery of this kind was made in the Turkish dominions.
There were doubtless potters at work in other towns in the sixteenth century, such for instance as Damascus, and it is highly
probable that they would adapt their wares to the prevailing

Turkish taste as expressed by the Isnik pottery. But of this we
have no certain information; and for the present Isnik holds the
centre of the stage.

Turkish pottery is well represented in Bays XXVII and XXVI,
Cases D, E, F and A, B, C. We have already discussed the early
blue and white types such as figs. 93 and 94. The other blue and
white is merely a variety of the late sixteenth-century Turkish

FIG. 99. Turkish pottery dish. 16th century.

wares of Groups I and II, and it has the same designs as these,
expressed in light and dark blues instead of polychrome.

The polychrome Turkish pottery is unsurpassed for boldness
of design and brilliance of colour. It is at its best in the splendid
wall tiles which line the Turkish mosques and public buildings.
A few of these tiles are to be seen in Bay XXVII and on the Bridge,
but in the British Museum Collection the ware is chiefly represented
by articles of daily use. The majority of the specimens belong to
Group I, of which the distinguishing feature is a thick, upstanding
but vivid red.   This colour is obtained from a clay called Armenian bole, and it is applied in the form of a slip,[1] hence its thickness.

[1] Slip is liquid clay.

It varies in tint from sealing-wax red to orange and maroon. That this effective and characteristic Turkish red was rarely used on any other kind of pottery is not because it was unknown before the sixteenth century or because it afterwards became what the popular writer loves to call a 'lost art'. It was still in use at Kutāhiya, one of the localities in which the Armenian bole is found, in the first decade of the twentieth century; it appears on the so-called Kubatcha pottery in a rather anaemic tint; it was used by Mesopotamian potters at Rakka in the twelfth century (see p. 21), though in very limited quantities; and it plays a part in the decoration of some of the tenth- or eleventh-century Byzantine pottery which has been found at Constantinople.[1]

Other colours employed in the decoration of this group are dark and light blue, turquoise green and leaf green, white slip, and a black pigment which is used for outlines. Gilding is occasionally added. As a rule the designs are outlined in black on the fine white ground, filled in with colour, and covered with transparent glaze. Occasionally the white background is coloured blue, green, or red, or more rarely the whole surface is coated with a coloured slip—maroon red, salmon, or lavender blue. In this latter case the design is applied in coloured slips or in a white slip which may or may not be painted with colour (fig. 102).

As already said, the outstanding feature of the decorative designs on this group of ware is a naturalistic rendering of flowers. On dishes they are seen growing from a common root on the edge of the well and spreading over the central space—tulips, hyacinths, roses, Martagon lilies, carnations, harebells, fritillaries, &c. A favourite trick of the painter was to represent the end of a tall spray as bent over and broken, as if it had been forcibly brought within the circumference of the dish. Sometimes the main design consists of an elegant branch covered with small blossoms, or again it is a pot of flowers. But besides the highly naturalistic flora of this ware, there are formalized lilies, fanciful palmettes inset with blossoms. lily scrolls, rosettes, cypress-like trees drawn out of scale, and long, graceful, feathery leaves, all of which are more or less conventional in treatment. Then there are geometrical patterns into which the floral designs are woven; cloud patterns; and diapers of blossoms, overlapping leaves, and scale patterns. Animals and birds occasionally figure in the decoration —deer, hare, hounds, and certain purely fantastic creatures. On a few specimens Turkish sailing boats form the motive; and occasionally a shield of arms is introduced. The human form is practically unknown except in a few later specimens which were doubtless made for Greek or Armenian Christians. There are

---

[1] See Talbot Rice, *Byzantine Glazed Pottery*, who hazards the suggestion that this early polychrome pottery may actually have been made at Nicaea (Isnik).

PLATE XXVIII

FIG. 101. TURKISH DISH: SIXTEENTH CENTURY

PLATE XXIX

FIG. 102. TURKISH JUG: SIXTEENTH CENTURY

PLATE XXX

FIG. 103. TURKISH DISH: SIXTEENTH CENTURY

PLATE XXXI

FIG. 104. TURKISH VASE: SIXTEENTH CENTURY

PLATE XXXII

FIG. 105. TURKISH TANKARD: SIXTEENTH CENTURY

PLATE XXXIII

FIG. 106. TURKISH BOWL: SIXTEENTH CENTURY

PLATE XXXIV

FIG. 107. TURKISH JUG: SIXTEENTH CENTURY

PLATE XXXV

FIG. 108. TURKISH BOTTLE: SIXTEENTH CENTURY

three examples of this later type in the Collection, on one of which is a tower and the date 1666 (fig. 109), on another a hand in the attitude of blessing and a Greek inscription with date 1667, and on the third a group of the Virgin and Child.

Certain border patterns recur, especially on the rims of dishes. One consists of overlapping petals, another of wavy lines enclosing divided blossoms, another of the same half-blossoms enclosed by a triangular arrangement of leaves, and another of lily scrolls;

Fig. 109. Turkish pottery dish dated 1666 A.D.

and perhaps commonest of all is the border of so-called 'Ammonite' scrolls broken by irregular panels with plant designs.

Various explanations have been given of the motive underlying this last border pattern (fig. 98), such as Chinese cloud scrolls, ammonite shells, Indian corn cobs, the last being the simplest and most probable. On the under sides of dishes there are usually a few widely spaced ornaments such as a row of alternating crocusheads and rosettes, or tulips and trefoil sprays.

It would be interesting to know where and how the highly individual type of decoration on this Turkish pottery was evolved. Of the naturalistic flowers some at least were native to Turkistan and were brought thence by the Turks. The arrangement of palmette-like flowers, flowering branches, and cypress trees may be observed in a carpet in the Louvre to which is ascribed a Persian provenance and a date in the second half of the sixteenth century. But we have still to decide the question whether the pottery designs were inspired by those of the rugs, or whether the splendid pottery wall decoration inspired the masters of textile hangings and carpets. The fact remains that this pottery is stamped with a character both in its colouring and its designs which differs widely from that of the Persian wares, and we can only regard it as an expression of Turkish taste,[1] and as a style which was evolved at Isnik in the middle of the sixteenth century.

The dating of this group is determined by the history of various buildings on which the tiles were used for wall decoration, such as the Piali Pasha Mosque in Constantinople (1565–1570), the Shāh-zādeh Tower built by Sulaimān I about 1550, and many other buildings of the second half of the sixteenth century. There are besides a few specimens with European metal mounts, such as a jug in the Franks Bequest with English mount dated 1597/8.[2] In the Exhibition of Moslem Art at The Hague in 1927 there was a silver cover, evidently from a Turkish jug, with inscription ' *Zu Nicea bin ich gemacht, und nun gen Halle in Sachsen bracht anno 1582* '.

It is generally agreed that the best period for this ware was the last half of the sixteenth century; but it evidently varied much in quality at all times, for a jug in the Collection with a Turkish poem dated 1560 is as coarse in make as the Christian plates dated 1666 and 1667 (see above), while on the other hand the quality of the red and of the other colours in the decoration of a fire-place[3] in the Victoria and Albert Museum is very high, although the piece is actually dated in the year 1731.

The shapes of Turkish pottery are simple: a variety of dishes, flat-bottomed, saucer-shaped, with wide or narrow rim, and a few with small, deep, central wells and wide, flat rims like the Italian *tondino*; slender-necked bottles of Persian form; jugs, pear-shaped, or globular with cylindrical necks; bowls; covered bowls on high feet; lamps, and occasionally vases. The cylindrical, tankard-shaped vessel (fig. 105) with disproportionately small handle was used as a flower vase; and there is one vase in the Collection with pierced shoulder, apparently intended for *pot-pourri*.

At present we know little about the extensive pottery manufacture which existed in the Golden Horn district of Constanti-

---

[1] Some writers who cannot bring themselves to believe that any artistic inspiration could have come from the Turks, have suggested that the taste for naturalistic flowers was inspired by the Italians who traded in Turkey. If this is so, it is curious how little this particular taste is reflected in contemporary Italian pottery.

[2] *Franks Bequest of Silver Plate in the British Museum*, Pl. XV.

[3] Formerly in the palace of Fu'ād Pasha in Constantinople.

nople in the seventeenth century. Evlia Tchélébi, who wrote at
that time, refers to two hundred and fifty potteries established
in the Golden Horn quarter and engaged in making 'drinking
vessels, jugs and bottles the like of which exist only in Chinese and
Nicaean ware'. The high quality of the pottery is testified by
the further statement that it
included 'jugs for which people
paid fourteen to fifteen piastres
to present to the sovereign and
viziers'.

Excavations made in the
district showed a recurrence of
fragments of typical Turkish
ware with a peculiar design of
spiral wreaths in blue precisely
similar to that of fig. 110. On
the strength of this evidence
pottery of this type is generally
assigned to the Golden Horn
factories.

An attempt to revive the
glories of the old Turkish
pottery at Constantinople was
made at Tekfour Serail in 1726.
The Grand Vizier Damad Ibra-
him Pasha brought a few potters from Nicaea, which though
in a decayed state was still
described as the 'cradle of the
art', and started a factory
which produced indifferent
wares in the old style.

Potters' marks do not appear
to have been used at Isnik, and
we must regard as something
quite unusual the sign (Pl.
XXXIX) painted in black on the
base of the *pot-pourri* vase just

Fig. 110. 'Golden Horn' pottery
bottle. 17th century.

mentioned. It resembles a cross with the letter S on its shaft, and
recalls the pharmacy marks on Italian drug-pots. A lion mask
on fig. 108 and an impressionist sketch of a human figure on a
jug may be regarded simply as *jeux d'esprit*.

KUTĀHIYA

Kutāhiya, a Turkish city with large Armenian settlements, is
situated in central Anatolia. Evlia Tchélébi, writing in 1671,[1]

[1] See Migeon and Sakisian, *op. cit.*, p. 45.

remarked that 'bowls, cups and drinking vessels of all sorts, jugs, pots and dishes' were made at Kutāhiya: but that the manufacture was not peculiar to this district, as the polychrome bowls of Nicaea are equally world-famed. Dr. Martin, who described in 1909[1] a recent visit to the place, stated that the clay for pottery is found close to the town, as is also the material for the thick red colour; but he was unable to find any ceramic traditions going back more than two centuries.

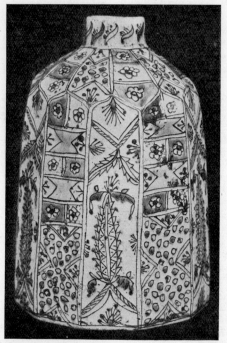

Fig. 111. Kutāhiya canister. 18th century.

Reasons have already been given (p. 81) for rejecting the theory that an important group of blue-painted Turkish pottery of sixteenth-century date was made here; and the only type which can be confidently assigned to Kutāhiya is that illustrated by fig. 111. This kind of ware is still made in the district, and a specimen of it dated 1719,[2] a saucer dish with figure of St. Sergius, takes it back almost to the days of Evlia Tchélébi.

The typical Kutāhiya ware is a sandy white material with silicious glaze, similar to the Turkish pottery but lacking the purity of the finer specimens of the latter. It is, however, thinly and crisply

[1] *Burlington Magazine*, Aug. 1909.   [2] Kelekian Collection, *op. cit.*

potted. The decoration is in blue, green, yellow, dark manganese purple, and an indifferent Turkish red. It is usually outlined in black and consists largely of palmettes and floral sprays, occasionally of figures. The general impression is of crude and confused designs, but gay and rather pleasing coloration. Marks are frequent, but they are uninstructive, chiefly consisting of criss-cross signs, leaf shapes, and discs surrounded by rays and dots.

It is in fact a quite characteristic, though undistinguished, ware, differing much in style, if little in technique, from the Turkish pottery of the fine period. Perhaps the most distinctive feature of its colour scheme is the prominence of yellow.

FIG. 92. Jar (*albarello*) of sandy white pottery painted in blue under a clear glaze in the style of Chinese Ming blue and white porcelain. Asia Minor. 15th century. H. 7·8 in.

FIG. 93. Lamp of impure white, sandy ware with dressing of white slip, painted in dark and light blue under a clear glaze. Probably Isnik. About 1500. H. 8·7 in.

FIG. 94. Bowl of impure white, sandy ware with dressing of white slip, painted in dark and light blue under a clear glaze. Under the base is a medallion with arabesques and formal flowers reserved in a blue ground. Probably Isnik. About 1500. D. 16·75 in.

FIG. 95. Jug of impure white, sandy ware with dressing of white slip, painted in two shades of blue under a clear glaze. Isnik. 16th century. H. 6·8 in.

FIG. 96. Jug of similar ware, painted in blue, sage green, and pale manganese purple, with black outlines. Isnik. 16th century. H. 9·7 in.

FIG. 97. Jug of similar ware painted in blue, sage green, and thin red slip, with black outlines. Isnik. 16th century. H. 10·6 in.

FIG. 98. Dish of similar ware painted in blue, sage green, and thick red, with details in manganese brown, under a clear glaze. 'Ammonite' scrolls on the rim. Isnik. 16th century. D. 11·85 in.

FIG. 99. Dish of similar ware painted in two shades of blue and turquoise, the designs outlined in black, with carnations, lilies, and tulips; one of the stalks is broken to fit into the side of the dish. Isnik. 16th century. D. 11·2 in.

FIG. 100. Mosque lamp of impure white, sandy ware dressed with white slip and painted in blue and turquoise green, with black outlines, under a clear glaze. The inscriptions in the main bands are passages from the Koran. Those on the foot contain the following— 'in the year 956, in the month of Jumāda al-ūla. The painter is the poor, the humble Muṣṭafa'. From the Mosque of Omar in Jerusalem. H. 15 in.

The date corresponds to June, 1549 A.D., the time when Sulaimān the Great restored and redecorated the Mosque of Omar.
See coloured postcard B 133.

FIG. 101. Dish of similar ware painted in dark blue, turquoise blue, and sage green. In a central medallion are a ewer in green and flowers in blue, green, and white in a dark blue ground. On the sides are floral medallions in a turquoise ground: and on the rim are blue and green rosettes and white tulips in a dark blue ground.
Isnik. 16th century.   D. 15·6 in.
See coloured postcard B 134.

FIG. 102. Jug of impure white, sandy ware with dressing of white slip, painted in white slip, blue, and brown under a clear glaze, the background being coloured maroon red.
Isnik. 16th century.   H. 10 in.
See coloured postcard B 137.

FIG. 103. Dish of similar ware painted in blue, green, and thick red with black outlines under a clear glaze.
Isnik. 16th century.   D. 11·65 in.
See coloured postcard B 136.

FIG. 104. Vase of similar ware painted in blue, green, and thick red with black outlines under a clear glaze, with lily scrolls in a deep blue ground.
Isnik. 16th century.   H. 10·5 in.
See coloured postcard B 135.

FIG. 105. Flower vase, tankard-shaped. Sandy, buff-white ware dressed with white slip and painted in blue, green, and thick red, with black outlines, under a clear glaze. 'Cypresses', roses, and palms.
Isnik. 16th century.   H. 9·85 in.

FIG. 106. Covered bowl of impure white, sandy ware dressed with white slip and painted in blue, turquoise green, and thick red, with black outlines, under a clear glaze. Tulips, carnations, &c.
Isnik. 16th century.   H. 8·95 in.

FIG. 107. Jug of impure white, sandy ware dressed with white slip and painted in blue, green, and thick red, with black outlines, under a clear glaze.
Isnik. 16th century.   H. 16·2 in.

Fig. 108. Bottle of similar ware painted in blue, green, and thick red, with black outlines, under a clear glaze. On the body and neck are *sīmurghs*, animals, and birds in a deep green ground. On the base the decorator has sketched a lion mask in black.
Isnik. 16th century.   H. 14·2 in.
Cf. coloured postcard B 138.

FIG. 109. Dish of sandy buff-white ware with wash of white slip, painted in dull purplish blue, green, and thick red, with black outlines, under a clear glaze. The Greek inscription on the rim means 'Lord! Lord! Turn not thy face from us. May 25 year 1666'.
D. 10·3 in.

PLATE XXXVI

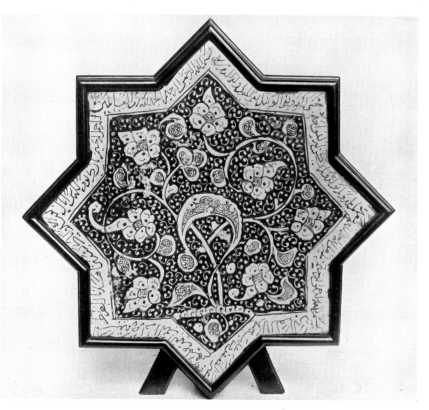

FIG. 112. TILE FROM VERAMIN. ABOUT 1262

Fig. 110. Bottle of impure white, sandy ware dressed with white slip and painted in blue and turquoise under a clear glaze. Golden Horn type. 17th century. H. 17 in.

Fig. 111. Canister of sandy white ware painted in blue, turquoise, yellow, and thick red, with black outlines, under a clear glaze. Kutāhiya. 18th century. H. 6·2 in.

TILES

The use of glazed pottery for wall decoration dates back to Achaemenian times in Persia. The famous frieze of glazed bricks found at Susa and now in the Louvre was doubtless not a solitary instance, and we may regard the glazed tiles with which the buildings were decorated in Islamic times as its lineal descendants.

The earliest of these known to us are the wall tiles found at Sāmarrā, large slabs about $10\frac{1}{2}$ inches square and oblong hexagonal border tiles to surround them. The squares are painted with designs in red, green, and golden brown lustres, or in a heavy dark brown which may have once been lustrous but now is dull. The hexagons are coloured with green, yellow, and brown glazes, or mottled with flecks of lustre pigment on a creamy white glaze. Fragments of them are to be seen in the Table-case in Bay XXVII. Fig. 8 is part of a square with a lustre design of a cock enclosed by a wreath; fig. 9 is painted in dark brown with part of a continuous scroll which extended over a series of square slabs.

These specimens show that tilework of a highly artistic kind was in use in the ninth century. Further confirmation of this is given by the square tiles which decorate the mosque of Sidi Ocba at Kairuan in Tunis. They are decorated with elaborate lustre patterns (each tile complete in itself) which have the closest analogies with the lustred pottery found at Sāmarrā; and the tradition that these tiles were brought from Bagdad[1] in 894 is certainly supported by stylistic considerations.

The star-shaped tile, the most characteristic form in later Persian tilework, does not appear at Sāmarrā or at Kairuan; but it must at any rate have come into being soon after the Sāmarrā period, for a star-tile with iridescent blue glaze, in the Freer Collection at Washington, bears the date = A.D. 947. Next after this comes a turquoise-glazed star-tile in the Kelekian Collection, with the date, = 1121 A.D., in raised characters. The typical star-tiles are eight-pointed, and they are fitted into a pattern by means of cruciform tiles (fig. 113).

In the thirteenth and fourteenth centuries the mosques and

---

[1] G. Marçais, *Les Faïences à Reflets Métalliques de la Grande Mosquée de Kairouan*, Paris, 1928, p. 10. The text on which this tradition rests mentions two sets of tiles, one which was imported by the Emir from a source not named, and the other which was made by a 'man from Bagdad'.

public buildings in Persia were resplendent with tile decoration
in lustre, blue and lustre, or Rhages polychrome enamels on cream,
turquoise, or dark blue grounds, even in surface or moulded with
low reliefs.

Yākūt, writing in the early thirteenth century, describes
Rhages as a 'magnificent city having its houses covered with
brilliantly glazed and coloured bricks'. Ibn Baṭūṭah in the middle
of the fourteenth century describes wall decoration of glazed tiles

FIG. 113. Lustred tile from Veramin. 13th century.

at Meshed 'Alī, Ispahan, Tabriz, and Kallat. He calls this pottery
Kāshānī, or ware of Kāshān, a place which seems to have been
famed for its pottery as early as the beginning of the thirteenth
century.

There is no lack of dated examples of the tilework of our second
period, i.e. thirteenth to fifteenth century, especially in lustred
tiles. H. Wallis (*Persian Ceramic Art*, Pl. I) illustrates a star-tile
which is painted in blue and lustre with two hares and arabesque
foliage and an inscribed border with date=A.D. 1217.

Fig. 112 is a typical specimen from the Mosque at Veramin,
which was built in 1262. The lustred Veramin tiles are among
the finest examples of this kind of workmanship, painted in
brilliant lustre with a sure touch, the designs finely conceived and
executed. The main decoration is usually reserved in a lustred

PLATE XXXVII

FIG. 114. MIḤRĀB TILE: THIRTEENTH OR
FOURTEENTH CENTURY

PLATE XXXVIII

FIG. 115. MIḤRĀB TILE DATED 1310

ground which is etched over with curled scrolls. This technique is characteristic of the period and is observed on the thirteenth-century bowls and vessels found at Rhages and elsewhere.

It was soon discovered that raising parts of the design in relief helped the play of the lustre reflections, and we find these reliefs a constant feature of the large miḥrāb slabs (fig. 114) such as that in Case C of Bay XXVII, and the two on the adjoining pillar which were made in A.D. 1310 (fig. 115).

FIG. 116. Tile, dated 1328/9.

Other dated tiles in the Collection are fig. 116, which is reputed to have come from Teheran, dated 1328/9; fig. 117 with human figures, dated 1338/9; and fig. 118 with the Chinese design of a phoenix and plants, dated 1408.

As already noted, Chinese influences became particularly prominent in Persian decoration after the Mongol invasion of the thirteenth century. There is a dark blue miḥrāb tile on the column between Bays XXVII and XXVIII, which has a dragon and phoenix in relief along the upper border. This tile is painted with supplementary designs in red and white enamels in the Rhages style: and on the southern face of the same pillar is a panel of two oblong tiles with dark blue glaze similarly painted in red and white but with the addition of leaf gilding.

Gold plays a more prominent part on a few tiles of this class
which are exhibited on the Bridge; and we are told that similar
dark blue and gold tiles were used in the interior of the Blue
Mosque of Tabriz, which was not built till 1438.

TILE MOSAICS

The use of mosaics of glazed pottery is a feature of Near-
Eastern wall decoration. It may be said to have begun with the

FIG. 117. Tile dated 1338/9.

embedding of glazed bricks in the wall surface, as in the Achaemenian friezes at Susa. A further stage is reached in the cutting
of glazed slabs into a pre-arranged pattern and embedding them
in plaster on the wall. Eventually we arrive at the elaborate
Persian mosaic in which the most intricate floral scroll-work,
background and all, is cut out of glazed slabs and fitted together
on the wall surface. This elaboration of the process was reached
towards the end of the fourteenth century. Good examples of the
second stage are to be seen on the Seljuk buildings of Asia Minor:
but it is evident that the art came from farther East, for the
signature of a Mosul artist occurs on a brick from a mid-thirteenth-

century building at Konia,[1] while the Sirtchali Médressé (1243) in the same city bears the inscribed name of Muḥammad, son of 'Uthmān, the architect of Ṭūs, in Khorāsān.

Mosaics have been found in the old Seljuk city of Sulṭān-Kala in Merv, at Meshed in Khorāsān, at Tabriz (late thirteenth century), at Sulṭānīya (early fourteenth century), on the tomb of Tamerlane at Samarkand (1413), and in the same city as late as 1598.

FIG. 118. Tile dated 1408.

The colours of the early mosaics are dark blue, turquoise, white and black, some of the earliest being in blue alone. Yellow, brown, and green were added in the latter part of the fourteenth century.

There are only a few fragments in the Collection to illustrate the Persian mosaic and they are exhibited on the Bridge. They include three pieces from the famous Blue Mosque of Tabriz, which date from about 1438. Good examples of similar tilework from Ispahan may be seen in the Victoria and Albert Museum.

At a later period, in the sixteenth and seventeenth centuries, recourse was had to a simpler technique which produced the general appearance of mosaic while avoiding the difficult process

[1] Migeon and Sakisian, *La Céramique d'Asie-Mineure et de Constantinople*, p. 7.

of inlaying. The designs were in fact painted in coloured glazes, a dry channel being left round the edges, as in the *cuerda seca* tiles of Spain, to suggest the edges of mosaic inlay. Later still this imitative work was further simplified by painting outlines in manganese in place of the dry borders, the design being simply painted in colours in a flat surface and covered with a single wash of glaze.

The pottery wall tiles naturally followed the changing fashions and those of our third period differ widely in style from the tiles of Veramin and Rhages. Lustre had not entirely ceased to be used for wall decoration, as may be seen in the fragmentary tile in the Table-Case of Bay XXVII which is decorated in the fashion of the seventeenth-century lustre dishes. But lustred tiles of this time are exceedingly rare.

A splendid panel of painted tiles in the Victoria and Albert Museum reflects the taste of the seventeenth century. It is painted in blue, yellow, and white with ladies receiving visitors in a garden. A common variation of this kind of tile has figures of men hawking on horseback, and of ladies, raised in relief on a blue ground in which plants and trees are reserved. Shades of blue and black are the principal colours used, but sometimes yellow is introduced. Specimens of small tiles of this type may be seen on the Bridge. They have been made continuously from the seventeenth century to the twentieth.

In the same Case on the Bridge are other examples of later tilework. Some have figures in relief painted in Chinese *famille rose* colours on an opaque white ground; and others are painted on the flat in blue, green, manganese, and turquoise with busts of Persian men and women in frame borders. Both types belong to the late eighteenth or early nineteenth century.

The beautiful tilework which played such an important part in Turkish architecture has been discussed in a previous chapter.

FIG. 112. Star-tile of sandy whitish pottery with opaque creamy glaze painted in golden brown lustre with coppery reflections. The central design is reserved in a ground of lustre which is etched with scrolls. Koranic inscriptions in Naskhi characters in the border. From the mosque at Veramin. About 1262.

FIG. 113. Cruciform tile of similar make; and part of a star-tile.

FIG. 114. Miḥrāb tile of sandy whitish pottery with opaque creamy glaze. The decoration is moulded in relief and coloured with blue, turquoise, and golden brown lustre, against a background of lustre etched with ornamental patterns.
13th or 14th century.   L. 12 in.
    See coloured postcard C 203.

FIG. 115. Tile of similar ware with decoration in relief and coloured with blue and lustre against a background of lustre diapered with

PLATE XXXIX

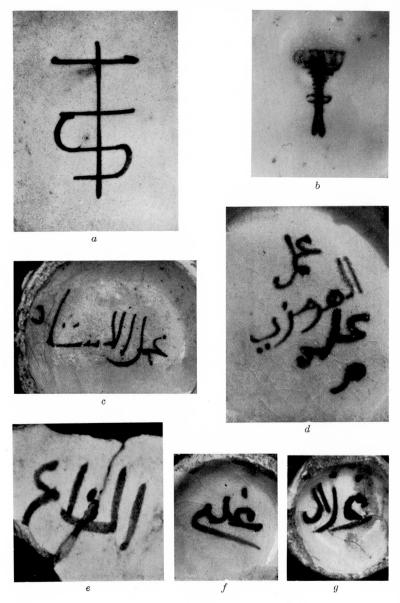

MARKS

reserved floral ornament and scrolls, in which there are occasional touches of blue.

Dated ' 1st Sha'bān 709' (=A.D. 1310).   L. 16·75 in.

FIG. 116. Star-tile of similar ware painted in blue and lustre, the lily design in relief. The inscription is dated A.H. 729 (=A.D. 1328/9). From Teheran.   L. 8·4 in.

FIG. 117. Star-tile of similar ware painted in blue and lustre. The inscription is dated A.H. 739 (=A.D. 1338/9).   L. 8·4 in.

FIG. 118. Star-tile of similar ware painted in blue and lustre with a Chinese 'phoenix' and an inscribed border containing the date A.H. 810 (=A.D. 1408).   D. 8·2 in.

MARKS (PLATE XXXIX)

A. Mark on Turkish pottery: see p. 91.

B. 'Tassel' mark on Persian pottery: see p. 77.

C. to G. Marks on Egyptian pottery, namely signatures of Ash-Shāmī (C), al-Hormuzī (D), al-Shā'ir (E, incomplete), Ghā'ibī (F) and Ghazal (G): see p. 60.

INDEX

PRINTED IN GREAT BRITAIN AT THE UNIVERSITY PRESS, OXFORD
BY JOHN JOHNSON, PRINTER TO THE UNIVERSITY